Keys to Reading

MYSTERIOUS WiSTERiA

Theodore L. Harris
Mildred Creekmore
Margaret H. Greenman

Harold B. Allen
Linguistic Consultant

THE ECONOMY COMPANY
Oklahoma City   Atlanta   Indianapolis

Permission to use or adapt copyrighted material appearing in this book is gratefully
acknowledged on pages 319 and 320, which are hereby made a part of this copyright page.

ISBN 0–87892–946–0

Contents

Hear Ye! Hear Ye!

The Wild Ones Stir

Somewhere beneath the Sun

Sing, City, Sing

Sea Mist

Straw into Gold

counter   stumbling   warden

bubbling   mattress   hobbled

sailors   motion   ruler

fuel   museum   recreation   crier

dislike   display   disappear

lantern

messenger

Salem

India

disappeared

unusual

shadows

Great Day at Salem

7

Old Jacob was busy working in his store when a messenger boy from the ship *America* ran in.

"There is a strange and wonderful gift for you aboard the *America!*" cried the boy. "We just arrived at the Salem dock. I ran to get you as fast as I could. Here's a note from Captain Blake, sir."

Jacob reached over the counter for the envelope, which was closed with a red wax seal. "Aha!" said the old man. "It's from Jim. Let's see what he has to say." He broke the wax seal, opened the letter, and read aloud,

> Dear Uncle Jacob,
>
> The ruler of India has endeared himself to me with an unusual present. Go to my friend, Captain Blake, of the *America*. The gift is aboard his ship. I send it to you with my best wishes.
>
> Your nephew,
> Jim

By this time the messenger could hardly stand still. "He's right, sir," he shouted.

"It is indeed unusual! All of Salem is down at the dock waiting to see it."

Jacob grabbed his hat from the counter top and hobbled after the young sailor. At the noisy dock, they saw men, women, and children swarming about the ship.

Old Jacob pushed through the crowd. His eyes searched for the captain among the sailors on deck. "Hey, Captain Blake, where is my gift?" he yelled.

"You'll have to come down in the hold and get it, Jacob," the captain yelled back. The captain's blue eyes danced. "Come on up," he said. "There's nothing to be afraid of—not much!"

The sailors on deck laughed out loud.

Old Jacob saw he would have to go aboard. Breathing a deep sigh, he climbed up the rope ladder.

Helping him over the side of the ship, the captain took Old Jacob's arm to lead him to the hold. The old man backed away, but the captain finally got him down the steep ladder into the dark hold below. The only light came from one small lantern. Strange shadows swayed back and forth as the lantern swung with the slow rolling motion of the ship.

"There it is, Jacob," said the captain. He pointed to a huge crate in one corner.

Old Jacob's knees were shaking. He was afraid of this strange thing given to his nephew by the ruler of India.

The captain lit the candle in his hand and motioned for Jacob to come closer to the large box. Old Jacob hobbled slowly over to the corner. He was just about three feet from the crate when he saw something that made him gasp and step back in fright. Something long and gray and bigger around than a man's arm wriggled out between the slats of the box. It swung to the left and to the right. Then it slowly curled back and disappeared inside the box.

Jacob turned to run back up the ladder.

But the captain caught Jacob's coat and said, "It won't hurt you. In India people ride them and make pets of them."

The captain's hand stroked the long thing which curled about his arm. Jacob watched as the thick gray thing wriggled in and out between the slats. Finally he stepped into the shadows and stroked it, too. Soon all of Old Jacob's fear had disappeared.

When Jacob returned to the dock, a large crowd gathered around him.

"What's in the box?" asked one man.

"When can we see it?" called another.

Jacob winked at the captain. He quickly made plans for this unusual present.

"Tomorrow night. Come to the back of my store. For two pennies your questions will be answered," said Jacob.

The next night Old Jacob smiled as he listened to pennies drop on the counter. Then he listened to the gasp of each man, woman, and child as each saw for the first time his unusual present from India.

The present? Why, it was the very first elephant ever to be seen in America!

garbage pirate furnace
fifty clumsy mighty
dozen cousin soda grandson

village
Macy
mutton
earlier
harbor
sighting
hoarse
Folger
intended

Noisy Boy
from Nantucket

Peter Folger was looking out to sea from the top of his grandmother's windmill. He was pretending he was on a Nantucket whaler sighting a whale.

"Blo-o-o-ows, thar she blows!" shouted Peter in a mighty voice.

"You get down from there, Peter," Grandmother called. "Never have I heard such a noise! There is wood to chop. Get along now. And, grandson, try to keep your voice down. Have some respect for yourself."

Peter got off the windmill in a hurry. "Yes, Grandmother," he said politely.

But the words came out louder than he had intended. His grandmother threw her hands over her ears and hurried toward the house. "That noisy boy!" she said. "He makes twice the noise the Town Crier does."

Peter was glad Grandmother had made him think of the Town Crier. He decided to try to find Crier Macy down at the harbor and go through the village with him. Sometimes Mr. Macy let Peter ring the brass bell to alert the folks in Nantucket. Then Mr. Macy would cry out the news.

As Peter turned into Main Street, he met Mr. Macy.

"Thought you were a whaler sighting a whale," laughed Mr. Macy. "I'll make you a crier yet. Some folks are good at one thing, some at another. But come along. The ship from New Bedford will be late, and there's a meat auction tomorrow. I've got a cold and don't feel like making verses. But I'll make a few just to please folks."

Mr. Macy handed Peter the bell. After Peter rang it loudly, Mr. Macy threw back his head and shouted,

"Eight o'clock and all is well.
Stop your talking, hear me tell.
If you want news, you'll have to wait.
Ship from New Bedford's coming late.
Tomorrow at ten come down the street,
To the village circle to get your meat.
Beef and bacon, mutton and lamb,
Also an auction of good thick ham."

Up and down the streets went Peter and the Town Crier until the news was cried several times.

"Folks usually want to know about the ship, Peter," said Mr. Macy as they walked home. "Seems as if they need to get either on the Island or off again. Or they want the mail."

Mr. Macy turned in at his own gate. "Now get along with you, Peter," Mr. Macy said, "and help your grandmother. I won't cry the news again until this evening and then not much. I'm coming down with a cold, and I'm getting hoarse."

16

Peter didn't get back to the village that evening to see the ship come in. But he did hear Mr. Macy cry that it would leave at eight o'clock sharp the next day.

Peter liked to be on hand when the ship was ready to sail. So he got up with the sun the next morning. He ate a cold piece of mutton and drank a glass of milk. Then he hurried off to the harbor.

At the dock, mail and packages were being loaded. So Peter went right up to Captain Gardner and asked, "Any work, sir?"

Captain Gardner jumped. "You don't need to yell so loud, Peter Folger," he said. "We're getting under way earlier than we had intended. The wind has changed, and bad weather is blowing in from sea. I've sent word to Crier Macy to alert the town, but I haven't heard a thing from him yet. Run to his house and tell him again."

Mr. Macy shook his head sadly when he saw Peter. "I know the ship is to sail an hour earlier," he whispered. "But I can't tell folks about it. My voice is gone."

Peter nodded with understanding. "I'll tell Captain Gardner," Peter yelled, louder than he intended.

"No, no," exclaimed Mr. Macy in a hoarse whisper. "Anyone with a big bold voice like yours can do it himself. Get the brass bell from my table and get along and cry the news for me loud and clear."

Peter stood in front of Mr. Macy's house for a few minutes. Then he started up the street. He threw back his head, and out came a yell loud enough to wake Nantucket Island from end to end,

Wake up, folks, and don't be slow.
At seven o'clock the ship will go.
The wind is up, the weather is down.
She's sailing early for New Bedford Town.
It's Peter Folger, crying so bold,
Because Mr. Macy's home with a cold."

Peter cried up and down the streets until the whole town was awake. When he reached his own house, Grandmother was standing at the door. She looked as if she couldn't believe what she saw and heard. So Peter stopped at the gate and shouted with a mighty shout,

"Grandmother, Grandmother!
Come and hear
Your grandson Peter loud and clear.
He's not so much at cutting wood,
But when he cries, his crying is good."

When Peter looked at his grandmother, she was shaking her head. But there was a proud look on Grandmother's face.

"That noisy boy!" she exclaimed.

Think about This:

1 Why did Crier Macy think that Peter could become a Town Crier?
2 Can you think of times when having a loud voice might help you?
3 During the years of early America, why did the people need a Town Crier?
4 Why do we not have a Town Crier today?
5 As a Town Crier, what verses would you make?

We work with words.

express   explode   expect
safer   tasted   widest   staring

Sound the words.

except

bulging

loft

tiptoed

ox

bonnet

barefoot

Janey

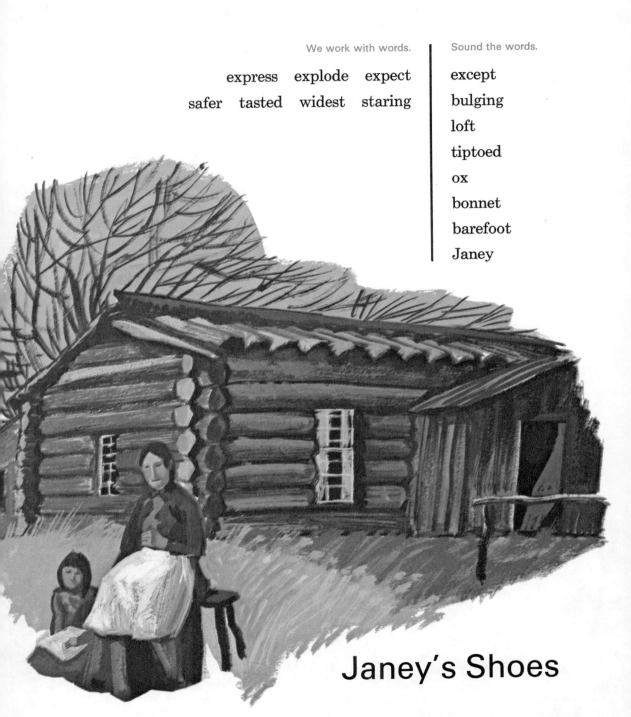

Janey's Shoes

Barefoot down the Road

Janey sat quietly and listened to Ma. "Pa has decided to move to the mountains where land is free," Ma explained. "He and I will go find a place. You must stay with the neighbors until we come back for you."

"When will you come, Ma?" Janey asked. But Janey's ma didn't answer.

"Be sure you take care of your shoes," Ma said as she was about to leave. "Winter isn't far off. I want to be sure you don't have to go barefoot." She had tears in her eyes as she kissed Janey good-bye.

Then Janey watched her folks leave. Pa walked ahead, and Ma sat in the ox cart wearing her black bonnet.

Janey saw all the family things bulging under the cover of the cart and the old cow following behind. A lump formed in Janey's throat. But she didn't say anything, and she didn't cry.

Janey got along somehow until night came on. Then she felt worse. The neighbor lady fixed her a small mattress in a loft above the kitchen.

In bed Janey lay wide awake. Everything seemed strange. The neighbor lady, lying on a mattress nearby, began to snore. Janey felt the lump in her throat again. "I want to be with Ma and Pa," she thought. "I just want my ma and pa."

She felt around for her dress and slipped into it. She climbed from the loft, tiptoed to the door, and pulled the latch.

"Oh, there's a bright moon," said Janey to herself. "And there's the shiny road that goes straight to my ma and pa!"

The dust felt cool to her bare feet, and the first thing she knew, she was following the road. She ran and ran until she was out of breath. Then she walked.

Janey came to a crossroad now and then, but she never turned off. Something seemed to tell her to keep to the widest road.

Janey walked all night long. Just before sunrise, a chill seemed to rise up out of the ground. For the first time, Janey felt cold and tired and afraid. It seemed that she would never catch up with her folks. And her spirit began to sink.

Somehow she kept going. "Surely Ma and Pa took the widest road," Janey thought.

Then up ahead, standing out against the sunrise at another crossroad, Janey saw a woman—a woman with a black bonnet. "Ma! Ma!" called Janey.

The woman looked around. Janey flew down the road to her. She kissed Ma and sobbed her heart out—all she had held inside the day before and all night on the road.

Then Pa came up with wood for the fire. He just stood looking at Janey, his eyes bulging, as if he were seeing a ghost.

"What are we going to do about her, Pa?" asked Ma.

Janey held tight to her ma's arm, a chill running through her. She shivered, waiting to hear what Pa would say. "Take me along, Pa," she begged.

"But you've got no clothes—except what's on your back," Pa said. "You're barefoot. You got no shoes. It's a rough trip."

"Your shoes, Janey! Where are they?" Ma cried, shaking Janey's shoulder.

Janey shook her head. She hadn't even thought of her shoes when she had tiptoed away from the neighbors.

"My feet are tough, Pa," she said. "And the clothes I got on are good enough."

Pa frowned. "I don't know, Janey. I don't know. We'll decide after breakfast."

Janey sat near the campfire and rested. "Surely they won't send me back!" she said to herself. "Not now!"

What a wonderful breakfast they had that morning! Janey sat on the cool ground with Ma and Pa. She had never tasted bacon so good. And she had never known how nice it was just to be with her ma and pa.

As they were cleaning up after breakfast, a man came by on a horse. Pa yelled and asked him to tell the neighbor lady where Janey was. "Just tell her that we're taking Janey along with us," Pa called.

"All right, Janey," Pa said then. "You'll just have to be tough and go without shoes. But it's not going to be easy."

shelves halves calves

pinned patting trapped

cherries emptied countries

knives

slipping

berries

cobbled

lean-to

oxen

yokes

sow

A Rough Climb

Janey, Ma, and Pa were a month traveling the two hundred miles to the mountains. The oxen were slow, and the road was uphill and often full of mud. One day they met a drove of hogs so large they had to wait nearly a day for the hogs to pass by. But the young sow they found the next day, lying beside the road, was well worth the wait.

"Let's take her along," Ma said.

"Guess we should," said Pa. "She'll die if we leave her here."

But they had brought along only enough food for the oxen and the cow. So every night Janey had to dig roots and look for berries to feed the sow. But Janey didn't mind. While the weather was warm, the climb into the mountains was really enjoyable. Down below them the country spread out, all blue and golden in the distance.

But soon the weather began to feel sharp. Janey kept warm by riding on the load and slipping her feet into the feather bed.

But when time came to make camp, Janey had to get down and look for berries. As it got colder and colder, she wished many times she had remembered her shoes.

At last they came to a small village, way up in the mountains. And Pa thought he'd better try to get some land not too far away. So for a few days he left Janey and Ma in the village. When he got back, he had a pleased look. He hitched up their oxen with the harness and wooden yokes. And soon they were on their way again.

They had not been traveling long when it began to snow. Sometimes Janey crouched in the cart with old covers around her while Ma and Pa struggled on, looking like two snow ghosts stumbling along.

But Janey could not ride all the time. Going uphill with the heavy load, the oxen kept stumbling and slipping in the snow. By nightfall, when they came to the last steep climb, the oxen were worn out. They stopped trying and just stood there panting.

"Can't push the oxen too hard," said Pa. "We're lucky they lasted this far."

He took off the clumsy wooden yokes and the harness. The oxen lay down right where they were, in the snow.

"We'll just leave them here for tonight," Pa said. "We'll go ahead on foot."

"What about Janey?" Ma asked.

"I guess she'll just have to stand it," Pa said. "It's not far now."

Janey sucked in her breath as she stepped down into the snow. It was so cold to her bare feet! But she knew nothing could be done about it. Pa was loaded down with all their food, and Ma was stumbling along with the feather bed and the covers. They began climbing.

"It's only about a mile now, maybe less," Pa said as if to give them strength.

But it seemed to Janey that the climb lasted a hundred years. The cold cut into her bare feet like knives. But she didn't cry, and she didn't say anything

Somehow they got to their land. Pa had built a lean-to, and there was a pile of wood waiting. Before long they had a fire blazing in the lean-to, and Janey sat down to warm her numb feet. But as the feeling began to return, sharp knives seemed to cut into her feet once again, and tears came to Janey's eyes.

"Take your feet away from the fire!" Ma called. Then she rubbed Janey's feet with snow. And after a while they were warm.

While they sat around the campfire, Pa told them his plans. "Over there will be the house. We'll put the barn over here. There's a spring for water out there." Pa sat on the ground and looked out over the mountains in the distance. Janey could tell Pa felt like a king.

Now they had a home, but Janey still had no shoes. There was no money to buy any, and they had nothing to trade.

Then one day the sow that Janey had taken the trouble to feed had some baby pigs. "I'll go down to the village and trade a pig for some shoes for Janey," Pa said.

So Pa hitched up the oxen and went to the village. But when Janey saw Pa coming back, she could tell he was disappointed. "Did you get the shoes, Pa?" she asked.

"No, Janey," Pa said. "There wasn't one pair in town that wasn't already on someone's feet. There just weren't any."

"Oh!" Janey said. "Oh, I see."

"But I got a cowhide. And after nightfall, I'll see what I can do."

Then every night, after pushing a plow all day, Pa sat and cobbled away. And soon Janey had a pair of cowhide shoes. They were clumsy. They didn't have any shine. But Janey had never in her whole life had anything she wanted so much as those new cobbled shoes.

That first night, while making plans, Pa had felt like a king. Now Janey had a pair of shoes. And she felt like a princess in her own little kingdom.

Velvet Shoes

Let us walk in the white snow
 In a soundless space,
With footsteps quiet and slow,
 At a tranquil pace,
 Under veils of white lace.

I shall go shod in silk,
 And you in wool,
White as a white cow's milk,
 More beautiful
 Than the breast of a gull.

We shall walk through the still town
 In a windless peace;
We shall step upon the white down,
 Upon silver fleece,
 Upon softer than these.

We shall walk in velvet shoes;
 Wherever we go
Silence will fall like dews
 On white silence below.
 We shall walk in the snow.

by Elinor Wylie

terrace pirate garbage

exchanged exercise expressman

tasty wiser trading

furnace

examined

described

glassmakers

Amsterdam

disk

roundels

cousin

shutters

Berkeley

Van Dyke

Gerrit

sash

Glassmaker's Street

Cities, like people, are always small when they are young. Even a great city like New York was once just a village with a dusty roadway and no sidewalks.

Long ago, when Gerrit Van Dyke lived near New York City, it was just a trading post called New Amsterdam. One of its grassy lanes was named Glassmaker's Street. On this lane glassmakers made glass bottles and windowpanes.

Gerrit lived with his mother in a small village called Berkeley Corners. And one winter's morning, Gerrit's mother held up a sheet of ice which had formed during the night in the water bucket.

"Look!" she called. "If this would stay frozen, we could have a sheet of glass for our window. It looks like the glass in our windows when I was a girl in Holland! It makes me homesick to look at it."

Then his mother smiled, but Gerrit knew she was close to tears. And he knew why. There were no glass windows in Berkeley Corners. The meeting house had oiled paper in its windows to let the light in. All the other houses, like his own, had to manage with wooden shutters. When it was cold, the shutters had to be closed. Then the houses were dark. It was no wonder his mother felt homesick and gloomy!

Suddenly an idea popped into Gerrit's head. He would find a way to get a glass window for his mother!

"I might be able to catch a beaver or two in my traps. Then I could dress the skins and maybe trade them for glass window-panes," thought Gerrit. "But where could I trade the skins?"

Gerrit decided to ask his schoolmaster. The schoolmaster ought to know.

Gerrit found that the schoolmaster was just the man to ask about windowpanes. He had three cousins who were glassmakers. They worked in New Amsterdam in a shop on Glassmaker's Street.

"You go ahead and set your traps," said Mr. Jacobus, the schoolmaster. "If you get some skins, we'll manage to trade them. I always do some trading in the spring."

When spring arrived, Gerrit had a fine pair of beaver skins to trade for glass. So with the schoolmaster, Gerrit went to New Amsterdam to do the trading.

Mr. Jacobus and Gerrit walked along the grassy lane and opened the shop door on Glassmaker's Street. Mr. Jacobus found one of his cousins setting small windowpanes into a window sash.

"Hello, Jacobus!" the cousin shouted. "The family has been looking for you this long while."

"I'm late this spring, but I've brought you a new customer," said the schoolmaster. "The lad here is Gerrit Van Dyke. It's his first trip to the trading post. Come, lad, speak up. Tell Evert that you would be a customer for his glass."

His cousin Evert laughed. "Jacobus always has a joke ready."

"Joke indeed! The lad has a fine pair of beaver skins to trade for a sash of glass. Speak up, lad—find your tongue!"

"Our meeting house in Berkeley Corners has oiled paper in its windows," Gerrit said slowly. "B-but I've never seen a bit of window glass before today. I want a sash of glass to take to my mother."

"What do you get for glass now?" asked the schoolmaster.

Evert replied, "Well, the glass for the church brought three beaver skins apiece, but—" He stopped and held up a sash and examined it.

"Hmm—most of that is made of roundels—
only three clear panes," said Jacobus.

It was hard for Gerrit to stay quiet. The
glass in the sash seemed a thing of beauty
to him. He had no idea what roundels were.
But the glass looked to him like what his
mother had described. He liked it!

"The roundels will let in light just as
well as clear glass," said Evert. "And
they cost much less to buy."

"We'll see, we'll see," the schoolmaster
said. "I want to visit with cousin Jan.
Take the lad to the furnace room and show
him what roundels are."

Inside the furnace room a group of men were at work next to a huge furnace. One workman was blowing through a long pipe. At the tip of the pipe dangled a large, orange-red ball of glowing hot glass. As he blew, the ball grew bigger.

"It's like blowing a soap bubble," said Gerrit.

"Now watch sharp!" called Evert. "You'll see a strange thing happen."

The next workman put the large bubble on a short rod. He made circles in the air and turned the rod, spinning the ball at the same time. He went slowly at first. Then he spun it faster and faster. Suddenly the ball flew open. Now it looked like a huge flat pancake!

41

"There you are!" shouted Evert. "When it is cool, it will be clear glass."

Evert brought a disk of finished glass. Gerrit examined it at close quarters.

"Now I know how the roundels get into glass panes," said Gerrit. "The lump in the middle is where the rod held the bubble. It was spun in circles to make the large round piece of glass."

"Yes, that lump is like a bull's-eye in the middle of a disk," said Evert. "The panes with the bull's-eye don't cost so much, you know."

When they returned to the front of the shop, the window sash was still lying on the counter.

"It's yours for two beaver skins, if you want it," said Evert.

"Yes, I want it!" said Gerrit.

The window sash was carefully bundled in blankets. But all the way home, Gerrit worried about the thick panes of glass— the roundels. His mother had said nothing about them when she described glass to him. She might not like them.

When Gerrit reached home, he gave his mother the gift at once.

"It's exactly like the ones we had when I was a girl in Holland—roundels and all!" cried Mother as she examined the sash.

Gerrit noticed a special smile on her face. "Come! Let's take down the wooden shutters right now and put in my beautiful glass window!" she said.

After that, the window became famous for miles around. Many people came to Berkeley Corners just to see the glass windowpanes that the boy, Gerrit, got for his mother from the shop on Glassmaker's Street.

THE WILD ONES STIR

midday midwinter midnight

beyond defrost musician patient

coyote

midway

delicious

circling

marmot

bobcat

sentry

colony

eagles

ledge

Bobcat
on the Run

45

The Hunt

A mother bobcat crouched on the ledge above her den. She was angry. A coyote was sneaking toward her den. The coyote knew there were bobcat babies in the den. And the bobcat kits would make delicious food for his own coyote pups.

It had been a terrible winter in these mountains. All the wild creatures were thin and hungry. Great numbers of small animals had died under the heavy snow. Now hostile creatures like the bobcat and coyote were fighting for the few small animals that could be found for food. Only the strongest and most clever creatures were still alive on the mountainsides.

Carefully the coyote came forward. Never before had the mother cat let him get this close. She must be gone. Now was his chance to get her kits.

The angry mother waited silently as the coyote came up to the den. Then she sprang from the ledge onto his back. The coyote yelped in pain as the cat's teeth sank into his neck. Then, with a firm grip, she sank her sharp claws into the coyote. He spun round and round, trying to throw her off. Then the terrified coyote quickly turned over on his back. This knocked the bobcat free. But the coyote still yelped loudly as he dashed down the mountainside.

The bobcat walked back to her den. She was sure the coyote would not return. Now she was ready to meet another problem. She must find food for her hungry kits.

After making sure her babies were safe, the cat left the den. She must now face a new danger—danger from the eagles.

47

A pair of golden eagles had a giant nest midway up one of the mountainsides. Like all the other creatures, the eagles were hungry. All day they kept circling high in the air, looking for food.

It was dark when the bobcat returned to the den from her hunt. She had hunted all the nearby places for squirrels or mice or marmots. But she had found hardly enough to stop the pain in her own stomach. Tonight the kits would have only the milk her thin body could give them.

Before sunrise the next day the bobcat set out for the other side of the mountain. She knew a colony of marmots lived there. It was far, and she would have to be gone too long. She worried about the coyote. And the eagles would be circling above the pass. But the kits must have food. So the bobcat had to chance that the dangerous trail through the pass would not be blocked by other hungry animals.

It was still dark when the mother bobcat passed the golden eagles' nest. By morning she was already near the marmot colony.

Quickly she spotted the marmot sentry on the ledge of a big rock. The bobcat did not try to hide. She kept walking up the trail. It was all part of her plan.

A warning whistle screeched in the air as the marmot saw the cat. He disappeared into a burrow under the rock. Silently the cat leaped to the hole. Then she crouched behind a rock to wait. The sentry would come out soon to see if all was safe.

At last the bobcat heard a soft scratch. The marmot was coming to the mouth of his burrow. Two anxious eyes looked all around. The sentry did not see the cat. He waited awhile in the mouth of his burrow. Then he climbed up the side of the rock.

Suddenly the cat sprang. It was over very quickly. There was a sharp cry. Then the grizzly marmot dangled silently in the cat's jaws.

Now the bobcat shivered with excitement. She must get home to her kits. With her jaws set in a firm grip on her delicious prize, she started up the trail.

Midway through the pass the bobcat came to a dead stop. There in the trail stood the coyote she had whipped the day before. And beside him stood his mate—the mother of his pups. The only trail back to the den was blocked.

robot chocolate buffalo
chosen safer glanced
madder trapped dropping

protect

escaped

pinned

coax

panic

snarled

signal

drift

expecting

attack

The Wait

The bobcat snarled at the two coyotes that blocked the trail. Then she turned back and leaped up on the sentry rock with her prize. Nothing could coax her to give up the marmot to those two coyotes. Her kits needed it for food.

The two coyotes sat down by the rock and looked up at the cat. They could not climb, and the bobcat could not come down. She knew she was pinned to the rock as long as she kept the marmot.

The coyotes held the mother bobcat there until the sun was high. It became very hot, and the rock burned the cat's feet. Soon the coyotes moved to a place in the shade. Each animal waited, expecting the other to signal the first move. It was a watching and waiting game.

Early in the afternoon the mother coyote stood up and stretched. The bobcat watched her set off up the trail. Was the mother coyote returning to protect her own pups? Or was the clever coyote hoping to coax her into a trap?

At last the cat could wait no longer. Her feet were burned from the hot rock. And she must get back to protect her kits. Taking a firm grip on the marmot, the cat glanced around, then jumped down from the rock. She snarled madly at the coyote. But he made no move to strike. He was dropping back to let her pass. She had escaped a battle—at least for now.

Once past the coyote, the bobcat began to run. The coyote was following her, but not too close. The cat was afraid the coyotes had coaxed her into a trap. But she had to go on, trapped or not.

From time to time the weary cat stopped to rest. The coyote stopped, too. But he did not come any closer. Now the cat was near the pass, and there she would be in even greater danger.

High in the sky the eagles moved in great circles. They were waiting for some animal to start across the bare mountain pass. The eagles began to drift to the south. If the bobcat waited until they were on the far side of their circle, she might make it to the bushes beyond the pass.

The bobcat waited for the turn that would signal her to go. When the right moment came, she raced down the long trail. The eagles were still circling to the south. And the coyote had begun to drift in closer from behind. Midway across the pass the cat glanced at the sky. One of the eagles was missing! A shadow flashed across the trail. The great golden eagle was dropping silently, quickly for a strike.

The bobcat raced madly ahead. At every leap she gave a gasp, expecting claws to tear into her back. Once again the shadow flashed. Then it disappeared. There was a scream of panic behind her. She made one last leap for the safety of the bushes. She had escaped the eagle!

Panting, the bobcat looked back along the trail. There was the coyote. The eagle had him pinned to the ground. Never again would the coyote come near her or her kits.

The weary bobcat paused long enough to catch her breath. She picked up the marmot and trotted toward her den. From the corner of her eye she thought she saw a flash of gray disappear around the bend.

In panic she dashed to her cave. But her eyes must have been playing tricks on her. It had not been the mother coyote. Her kits were safe.

Today she had brought home enough food. Tomorrow would bring another battle to stay alive. The coyote was gone. But the eagles would still make it dangerous to hunt on the mountainsides.

After nightfall, as soon as there was some safety from the eagles, she would look for a new den lower down on the mountain. It would be a long, weary night, moving the kits. But she would soon teach them to hunt. And it would be safer down there— much, much safer.

Think about This:

1 What is meant in the story when it says the bobcat was "pinned to the rock"?
2 Why didn't the coyote attack the bobcat?
3 When the mother bobcat saw "a flash of gray," what did she think she saw?
4 To what animal family does the marmot belong? The coyote?
5 What are some things being done to save wild animals today?

arrival musical natural
dislike discourage disagree
behave declare received

national
display
beneath
Mexico
ugly
Smokey
outrun
cub

The True Story of
Smokey the Bear

This is the story of a bear cub and how he won his fame—how he found a wonderful job to do, and how he got his name.

In a mountain forest in New Mexico, a bear cub lived with his mother. They made their home in a cozy cave that was near a stream.

Little cub had many lessons to learn. He learned to climb a tree when danger was near. He learned to reach into a hollow tree for fresh honey—and how to outrun the bees! The bear cub learned to turn over fallen logs to get the tasty bugs beneath. And he learned to fish, standing on a rock beside the clear stream.

The forest in New Mexico was never quiet. In the branches of the tall trees ran the chattering squirrels. From the stream came happy, bubbling sounds as it rushed by the bear's cozy cave. And above the bubbling, chattering noises came the songs and calls of the birds.

But one day the forest was alive with a different sound! Every animal was calling out its danger signal. And louder than the warning cries came a roar through the trees that hurt the bear's ears.

The little cub knew that danger was near, so he quickly climbed a tall tree. Then through the trees came a thick cloud of smoke that hurt the bear's eyes.

Beneath him other animals raced by in panic. Rabbits, mice, chipmunks, and wildcats with their kits—all scurried ahead to outrun the flames. But the bear cub just closed his eyes and held on to the tree as hard as he could.

All around him the forest fire roared. The flames licked at his fur and burned his paws. Still the cub stayed in the tree.

After a long time the noise stopped. The cub opened his eyes and looked all around. But instead of the green, grassy forest he was expecting to see, there was nothing except thousands of ugly black sticks. The fire had passed, and some of the black tree trunks were still smoldering.

The bear didn't see another animal anywhere. But soon he heard men talking. They were forest rangers who had just finished putting out the terrible fire.

"Well, look who's here," one ranger said. And he reached up and took the cub out of the tree. "What's your name, little cub— Smokey?" And from that day on, Smokey was the bear cub's name.

Although Smokey could not understand the man's words, he knew the voice was kind. The ranger stroked his fur and gave him cool water to drink. He put something on the bear's burned paws, then fed him tasty food from one of the packs.

Soon Smokey fell fast asleep. When he woke up, everything seemed strange to him. He was in a box that was to be his bed, soft with old blankets and a piece of rug. He was at the game warden's house.

Smokey had a fine time there at the game warden's house. Sometimes he played with the warden's little girl. But before long he was well enough to go to a new home— one just right for a bear cub.

Off in an airplane Smokey flew, all the way from New Mexico to Washington, D. C. When he was taken off the plane, someone put a forest ranger's hat on his head. Then newsmen crowded around him and took his picture. He was taken to the National Zoo and put on display so that all the people could see him.

Smokey's picture appeared in many newspapers, and his fame soon spread all over the country. Today he is known as Smokey the Bear. His pictures are on display in national parks and on television. Smokey helps people remember to be careful with fire when they are in the forest.

pollution   suggestion   collection

likable   workable   remarkable

rodeo   microscope   memory

protection

reasonable

pioneers

suggest

Andrew

heaving

froze

William

William Did It

63

Andrew and William were helping set up their tents for camping in the Great Smoky Mountains National Park.

"Now, remember," said Mom, "the ranger suggested we shouldn't bring food into our tents. The park bears usually eat from the garbage cans outside. But it's reasonable to suspect they'd come right inside a tent if they smelled food there."

Andrew laughed. "Can't you just see some clumsy bear stumbling over us as he claws around in our tent?" he asked William.

"Now don't frighten William," said Dad. "Just let the bears alone, and we'll all have a wonderful vacation. And, Andrew, I suggest you take care of your brother."

Next morning at sunrise the two brothers walked to the water pipe to fill their jugs before breakfast. There they met Gordon, a boy about Andrew's age.

"After breakfast, want to go down to the lake?" suggested Gordon.

"Can he come?" asked Andrew, pointing to William.

"Sure. But who's he?" asked Gordon.

"My little brother," answered Andrew.

"My name is William!" said William.

On the way back, walking with their jugs full of cold water, William said, "Can't you ever tell people my name? You always just say I'm your brother. And please stop telling people I'm little."

"I'm sorry. Honest," Andrew said. "But to me you're just my brother."

Soon the brothers felt like pioneers. They were used to having bears stroll near them in the daytime. But at night, if their flashlights showed a bear moving toward them, they would hurry off the path and wait for it to pass.

Every night William placed a hammer and an ax and a flashlight under his cot for protection. "I'll be ready if a bear comes," he said, "just like the pioneers."

Andrew always laughed at him.

One night Andrew was dreaming about a bear fight. Suddenly he sat up on his cot and listened. It wasn't a dream anymore. He heard a bear heaving and sniffing around outside.

In the darkness Andrew heard William sit up on his cot. "It's a bear," whispered William to Andrew. "A big one."

William was right. A big bear was close to their tent and moving closer.

Suddenly Andrew changed his mind about the ax William kept. All of a sudden that ax and hammer seemed very reasonable for protection against a full-grown bear. "Give me the ax," Andrew whispered.

"Oh, I forgot," whispered William as he slipped the ax to Andrew. "I've got part of an apple in my coat. I forgot to put it in a garbage can. Do you think that's what he's sniffing for?"

Andrew raised the ax. "Throw the apple! Quick. Out under the tent bottom."

"Don't hit him," begged William. "That won't kill him. He's a grown-up bear!"

"Throw out the apple!" said Andrew. "I'll just try to knock him out."

William threw the apple. Then he grabbed his flashlight and pushed it through the tent flap. The bear, huge and fierce, came out of the darkness, his sides heaving, his jaws open, and his long teeth glowing. Only three feet from the flashlight the bear froze, staring at the beam of light.

The boys froze and stared at the bear.

The whole night seemed to pass—until at last another light darted into the darkness. "What's happening?" called Dad as he poked a flashlight out his tent flap.

"A bear," the brothers called softly.

"Where?" shouted Mom.

"There!" yelled William, pointing his flashlight at the huge bear and staring after him. "Look, the flashlight frightened him. He's running away."

"William saved us!" yelled Andrew. "His flashlight stopped the bear."

The next day when Andrew told the story to Gordon, he never once said "my brother" or "my little brother." "William did it," he kept saying.

And that was the way Andrew always told the story after those camping days. It was always easy for Andrew to remember to say "William" after that.

Azor and the Turtle

Azor was in the third grade. He was good at skiing, at swimming, and at minding his own business. But there was one remarkable thing about him. Animals talked to him. They really did. And the things they said to him were important things.

Early one morning Azor saw his brother, Matthew, and Matthew's friend Jimmer starting down the street. He knew where they were going because they were carrying nets on long poles.

Matthew and Jimmer were going to Pirate Joe's Pond to catch turtles. They would sell them for twenty-five cents each.

Azor had always wanted to go along with them. If he could catch even one turtle himself, he would have twenty-five whole cents. Then he could go down to the store and, for once in his life, eat enough potato chips. But Matthew had always said, "You're too little. You'll only talk and scare the turtles away."

So Azor was very surprised when Matthew called to him, "Hey, Azor! You can come along if you want. We need someone to watch the box so they won't get away. We're going to stay all day. We'll catch a million! But remember now, no talking! Hear?"

Azor grabbed a piece of cake and a bottle of root beer. He raced after Matthew and Jimmer. When they got to Pirate Joe's, they hauled out a big box they had hidden there. It was just right to hold the turtles. They put it under a tree.

"Don't make a sound," Matthew warned. He and Jimmer left Azor sitting in the shade. They went down to the pond with their nets and threw some bread crumbs out. Then they waited for the turtles.

As Azor sat minding his own business, he thought of what his father had told him about Pirate Joe's Pond.

"I bet the bottom of that pond is covered with pennies!" his father had said. "Years ago, people used to go up to Pirate Joe's on a holiday. They ate cake and drank root beer. At night the women danced, and the men pitched pennies, it being a holiday and all. Of course, some of the men didn't win. Then they got very angry and tossed their pennies right into the water."

Pretty soon Matthew and Jimmer hauled some turtles up from the pond to put into the box. They sat and ate their lunches and drank their bottles of root beer.

"Jingoes!" said Matthew. "We've got seven turtles! You know how much that is? That's one dollar and seventy-five cents! And we have the whole afternoon to go!"

"If we get seven more this afternoon," Jimmer said, "it will be more than Billy's whole crew ever got in one day!"

"It won't be if you stay here all afternoon talking," said Azor.

So they went down to the water again and threw out more bread crumbs. It was around midafternoon when they brought two more turtles. Then there was a long time when they didn't bring any. Azor stretched out on his stomach and examined the turtles in the box.

There was a big turtle in there and two smaller ones. But the rest were tiny. Some of them had their heads and paws drawn into their shells and their pointed little tails wrapped across their bottoms. Others just crawled around and glanced at Azor.

73

Azor wondered how it was to be a turtle. And at that very second the biggest turtle blinked his eyes slowly and looked up at Azor in a remarkable way.

"Make it worth your while if you tip the box," he said. "The same time, same place, tomorrow."

Azor turned over the box. He watched the turtles crawl over the grass, their tails no longer wrapped across their bottoms, but wagging out behind. One by one they plopped into the pond. Azor was glad the tiny ones were going back to their mothers.

But when the last one had slid into the water, Azor suddenly thought of Matthew and Jimmer down by the pond. He started to feel quite strange. He thought it was probably time to go home. So he did.

Azor grew tired very early that night, because every place he went in the house, Matthew was there with his chin stuck way out and shaking his fist.

"What's the matter with you children?" his mother asked.

So Azor told her, and that made Matthew even madder. The second Azor saw him start getting madder and shaking his fist again, he remembered that his mother didn't like for Matthew to sell turtles.

After that Azor went to bed without having to be told.

The next day, around midafternoon, Azor hurried to get to the pond. He got there just in time to see the big turtle crawling up out of the water. The turtle had something in his mouth that looked like an old penny. Only it was much bigger—almost as big as a half-dollar.

The turtle blinked and dropped the coin in the grass in front of Azor. It was all wet and gunky, and Azor didn't even want to touch it, but he picked it up and put it in his pocket.

"Thank you very much," he called as the turtle was crawling back to the pond.

Then Azor went back home. After supper he went into the kitchen. He was shining the penny so it wouldn't be gunky and smell so awful, when suddenly his father came in. He watched Azor for a minute.

"Where did the penny come from?" asked his father.

"I got it up at Pirate Joe's Pond," Azor answered. But he didn't say anything about the turtle.

His father picked up the penny and looked at it.

"Hmmm!" he said. "I'm going to take this over to Lot Snow and see what he thinks. I'll be right back."

Azor knew that Mr. Snow liked old coins. He'd give twenty-five cents to anyone who brought him an Indian-head penny. But Azor had never had an Indian-head penny.

Azor was upstairs brushing his teeth when his father came back and called him in a loud voice—not an angry-loud voice, but a pleased-loud voice.

"Azor! Come down here!"

When Azor got downstairs, everyone was in the living room.

"Jingoes!" Matthew said, his mouth wide open. He was staring at a pile of money on the table.

"Well, Azor," his father said. "You're a rich man. That penny was very old—one of the first coins ever made in this country. Lot Snow bought it for FORTY-SEVEN DOLLARS! Pick the money up, son. It's all yours."

Azor picked it up. Except for the money for potato chips, the forty-seven dollars would go into the bank. Azor was saving to buy a horse when he got to be twelve.

Think about This:

1 Why did Matthew invite Azor along when in the past he had said Azor was too little?
2 Why do you suppose Azor went to bed without having to be told?
3 Why do you think Azor didn't tell Matthew or his father about the big turtle?
4 What are people called who buy old coins?
5 What do you think the boys hunted for the next time they went to the pond?

We work with words.

Sound the words.

dwarf   dwell   dwelling

accident   visitor   angrily

musician   patience   social

Sight word.

Schumacher

Dwight

alligator

especially

carpenter

received

expressman

eyelids

Little Alligator

79

One warm June morning, a large box was delivered to the home of Jimmie Voss. His big sister, Kay, looked at the box and then called to him, "It's for you, Jimmie. The expressman has brought you a box. It's from Uncle Dwight."

"Sign here, please," said the expressman. And Jimmie wrote his name on a piece of paper to show he had received the box.

"Be careful. He may bite," warned the expressman.

Jimmie peeked through the slats in the top of the box and jumped.

"Oh, Kay! It's a snake!" he cried.

Kay was quite grown-up, but she jumped, too, when she peeked inside. "Oh, Jimmie! We'd better get rid of him!" she cried.

Just then Mother came and pointed to the envelope tied to the box. "Let's find out what this is all about," she suggested.

Jimmie read the letter aloud,

Dear Jimmie,

I am sending you this baby alligator for a pet. See that he can get to water and give him raw meat to eat three times a week. Don't leave him out nights, for he's only a baby yet. And don't take him to bed with you, or you may wake in the morning to find a toe nibbled away.

Love,
Uncle Dwight

When they opened the box, the alligator looked around but made no move to get out. "I'll set up our pool in the backyard for him," said Jimmie. "Uncle Dwight said he should be able to get to water."

Soon the pool was all set. Jimmie put a block of wood in one end of the shallow water. Kay pulled a little grass and put it on the block. But no one made a move to pick up the alligator.

"He's your alligator, Jimmie," Kay said.
"It's your job to pick him up."

Jimmie looked at his mother. She nodded.
"Go ahead. He won't hurt you."

Jimmie looked at the alligator's rough
black and yellow skin. He looked at the
ugly blunt nose and queer eyes. Then he
looked at the mouth full of teeth.

"Well, go on!" Kay said. "We're waiting."

Jimmie shut his eyes and took hold of the
little alligator. Then he discovered a very
funny thing. He didn't mind picking it up
at all, especially since people were around
who were afraid to touch him.

Soon everyone in the neighborhood liked Jimmie's pet. They all wanted to feed it raw meat. But Jimmie had a rule that only he could feed the alligator.

"What are you going to name it?" asked Kay. "I'd call him Dopey if I were you. Look at him now! He surely is dopey!"

Jimmie said, "I'd like to name it after Grandpa Schumacher, even if he isn't my real grandpa. But it would be funny to name an alligator Schumacher."

Everyone agreed it would be funny.

Grandpa Schumacher thought it was funny, too—at first. But then he grinned and said, "It isn't so funny after all. Schumacher means shoemaker. And when the alligator grows up, maybe you'll make a fine pair of leather shoes from his skin."

Jimmie didn't think he'd do that, but he named his pet Schumacher anyway.

One day Jimmie and his friend David were watching Schumacher in the pool.

"Don't you think you ought to teach him some tricks?" asked David. "My dog, Butch, can sit up and beg for things."

"Schumacher can't sit up on his tail and beg," said Jimmie.

"No, but Butch rolls over and plays dead. Schumacher could do that," said David.

They tried to teach Schumacher to roll over and play dead. No luck! Schumacher got tired and snapped at Jimmie's finger.

Just then Kay walked up and looked into the pool. "Hey!" she said. "Your dopey pet has his eyes open under water!"

"Yes, it looks like he has windows over his eyes," said David. "Did you ever see such queer eyelids?"

Later Mother explained, "Alligators have an extra pair of eyelids, almost like clear plastic. That's why they can keep their eyes open under water."

One day Jimmie tickled Schumacher on his blunt nose with a blade of grass. The baby alligator wiggled his nose. What a funny grin! Jimmie tickled the alligator's nose again, and it did the same thing.

After that, Jimmie tickled Schumacher's nose with a blade of grass when he wanted him to show off.

The little alligator wasn't able to sit up and beg, and he couldn't play dead. But he did have one good trick!

When June was over, the Voss family moved to a new house. Jimmie didn't like leaving his friends, especially David and Grandpa Schumacher.

When the moving van was loaded, there wasn't room for Schumacher and his pool. "Never mind, Jimmie," said Mother. "He'll be all right here tonight, and we'll be sending back for him tomorrow."

The next day was a busy one. So they did not return for Schumacher until the second day. But then there was no trace of the little alligator or the pool. Schumacher had disappeared!

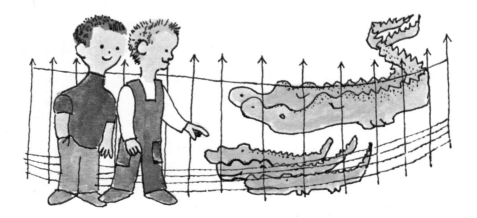

Jimmie asked all his friends. No one had seen a trace of the little alligator.

Days went by. Then Mother decided that a picnic lunch at the zoo might help Jimmie forget Schumacher for a little while. "I'll telephone and see if David and his mother can come, too," she said.

So off they went to the zoo. After lunch Jimmie and David looked at the alligators. The big ones lay in the sun, and there were three little ones near the fence.

"Say, doesn't that one in the middle look like Schumacher?" cried David.

"Yeah, it does," said Jimmie. "But baby alligators look pretty much alike."

"If only he was like Butch, we could call him and he'd come," said David.

"There he goes again," thought Jimmie, "talking about all his dog's tricks." Then Jimmie had an idea! He got a blade of grass and reached through the fence to tickle the nose of the middle alligator. It wiggled its ugly blunt nose and grinned!

"It's Schumacher!" yelled Jimmie.

"Better try the others," said David. "Maybe they all do that."

Jimmie tried to tickle the other two, but they just moved out of reach. Then the middle one crawled closer to the fence as if wanting his nose tickled again.

By this time Jimmie was jumping excitedly up and down, wanting to find the manager of the zoo. "Where's the manager's office, David?" he cried.

Away they raced and found the office at the far end of a building. "Why yes, we received that little alligator a week ago," the manager said. "A carpenter brought him in. Said he'd found him at an empty house when he went there to fix the steps. The carpenter brought him here, thinking the owner had left him behind."

"He's mine. We moved, and our van was too full," Jimmie explained. "And when we came back to get him, he was gone."

"How can you tell it's your pet?" asked the manager. He laughed when he heard about the alligator's funny grin.

How surprised their mothers were when the boys came back carrying Schumacher in a wooden box!

"It's good Schumacher visited the zoo," David said. "It may be his home someday when he gets too big for the backyard."

Jimmie nodded. "There's one thing for sure. He'll never be made into a pair of shoes—no matter what his name is."

usual   popular   museum

expecting   exercises   expensive

metal   arrival   coastal

ranges   whooping

pollution

extinct

natural

buffalo

swamp

dinosaurs

waste

wildlife

Animals in Danger

89

D. WISKUR

The world has always been in a state of change. Some changes have been good. Others have not been good. Many kinds of animals that once lived are not alive today because of changes made in their world. They have become extinct.

Millions of years ago dinosaurs roamed over the whole earth. Yet not one is alive today. The dinosaurs lived in warm swamps that covered the earth, and they fed on plants that grew in the swamps. Gradually the swamps became dry and cold, and the plants that fed the dinosaurs no longer grew. Without food, the dinosaurs became extinct. They could not live in their changing world.

Nature has brought some changes to the world of wild animals, but man himself has brought many of the changes. Wherever man has gone, he has taken over land that once belonged to wildlife. He has made a great many changes in the world about him so that he could live in comfort and pleasure. Too often these changes have killed the wildlife around him.

At one time millions of buffalo roamed the range in North America. Then man came and built fences across the open range. He killed buffaloes for food and sport. And soon the buffalo was almost extinct. The only buffaloes living now are in a zoo or on government or private game land.

Today man is changing the world faster than ever before. And wildlife is being robbed by these changes. Swamp land is being dried up to be used by man. This is taking away the natural home of alligators, turtles, and other swamp creatures. Men have made changes along our seacoasts, too. And these have robbed the whooping crane and other birds of their natural winter homes. Now many of these birds are becoming extinct.

Every day more people live on the earth, and they are building more and more homes on land that once belonged to wildlife. Miles and miles of highways are being built where animals once lived. Even such small animals as rabbits, squirrels, and skunks have a difficult time finding homes and safe places to hunt for food.

Already many of our wildlife creatures have no safe place. They are being killed by another change brought to their natural world by man—pollution. Pollution of water and air from man's insect sprays and waste matter has accidentally killed many fish and birds, such as the bald eagle.

Clean air and land and water are needed for any animal to stay alive. This is just as true of man as it is of the buffalo, the whooping crane, and other animals in nature. Animals can do nothing about their changing world. But man can. He can stop the use of harmful insect sprays. He can find ways to end pollution, so dangerous to living things. Perhaps in saving wildlife, man will help to save himself.

Buffalo Dusk

The buffaloes are gone.
   And those who saw the buffaloes are gone.
   Those who saw the buffaloes by thousands and
      how they pawed the prairie sod into dust
      with their hoofs, their great heads down
      pawing on in a great pageant of dusk,
   Those who saw the buffaloes are gone.
   And the buffaloes are gone.

by Carl Sandburg

forefoot   forenoon   foreleg

discount   discourage   displease

musical   social   politician

forehead

dislike

patience

behaved

ivory

china

declared

orderly

canal

teahouse

courtyard

sternly

Pepper Moon

by Esther Wood

No Place for a Dog

Pepper Moon was a young boy who lived in China. There was one thing he wanted more than anything—a dog. Every day Pepper Moon asked for a dog. And every day his family threw up their hands and said, "Pepper Moon! Don't ask for a dog! A dog would jump around and tear up shoes and knock over the china flowerpots!"

Pepper Moon's family was very orderly. This house was no place for a dog. And so Pepper Moon had no pets except the goldfish in the lily pool and such small creatures as he could hide.

One morning a terrible thing happened in that orderly house. The news was spread by the kitchen maids from courtyard to courtyard. "Third Mistress found a mouse in her sewing box!"

"A mouse!" The aunts and girl cousins shivered.

"In a sewing box!" Grandmother cried, putting down her teacup with a thump. "Now, indeed, something must be done!"

Grandmother called for her ivory cane. Then with the uncles and aunts behind her, she marched out to the lily pool in the courtyard.

"The time has come when something must be done about your pets!" Grandmother declared to Pepper Moon. "Whatever made you put mice in the sewing box?"

"Please," said Pepper Moon. "It was only one little mouse."

"And before that it was snails in the teacups," said Grandmother.

"Please," said Pepper Moon. "There were only two snails inside one teacup."

"And a frog in your father's shoe!" Grandmother continued.

"The frog didn't mean to get in Father's shoe!" Pepper Moon explained.

"Indeed, it is not pets that I dislike," declared Grandmother. "But you have such strange pets!"

"I'd really like a dog," Pepper Moon said hopefully.

"We must choose a pet that will suit us all!" said Grandmother sternly. "Now let me think what it shall be."

The family waited silently while Grandmother tapped her forehead with her jade ring and thought.

"A new goldfish would be nice," Pepper Moon's mother suggested at last. "Or maybe a cricket in a bamboo cage."

At that suggestion Grandmother's face brightened. "Now I know what would suit us all!" she cried. "A bird in a cage!"

Pepper Moon's heart sank. A bird could never take the place of a dog.

"Here are five pieces of silver," Grandmother said to Pepper Moon. "You have my permission to go to the bird market and choose any bird you like."

"Indeed, you may go all alone," Pepper Moon's father said.

Grandmother and the aunts and uncles and cousins sighed. "Now may we have peace from these snails and mice!"

Pepper Moon bowed and put on the coat he wore only on holidays. Then he ran to the big front gate and bowed politely to Old Tiger, the gatekeeper. "Today I'm going out alone," he called. "I have permission to buy myself a pet!"

"A dog?" asked Old Tiger excitedly.

"No," said Pepper Moon. "Only a bird."

"A thousand pities," said Old Tiger as he stroked the three long hairs that grew from his chin.

Pepper Moon bowed and hurried out into the busy street beside the brown canal. When he came to Camel Back Bridge, he looked into the canal. It was filled with boats—some stacked high with cucumbers and bags of white rice and some filled with squawking ducks and squealing pigs.

A barefoot farmer was carrying his fat brown ducks across Camel Back Bridge to the teahouse on the corner. When his back was turned, his two sons hid one of the ducks under a basket.

"Twenty, twenty-one," counted the farmer. Then he stopped and scratched his ear. "How now! One duck is missing," he said.

"It's Waddle-Tail!" cried the older boy. "Please don't take him to the teahouse and sell him for soup!"

"He's our pet!" begged the smaller boy.

"Squaw-w-wk!" cried Waddle-Tail.

Hearing all this, Pepper Moon decided that the one pet he would like to have was a duck. So he took a piece of silver from his purse and suggested that the boys sell him their pet.

"Waddle-Tail will never meet his end in a pot of soup," Pepper Moon promised as he started home with the duck.

Pepper Moon's duck was a surprise to the family, to say the least. The little girl cousins were delighted to hear the duck squawking. They brought an orange-red ribbon for his neck and a white jade bowl full of watermelon seeds.

Pepper Moon's mother and his aunts stood politely around Grandmother as she tapped her ivory cane on the floor and thought it over. No one in that orderly house had ever heard of a duck for a pet. No one knew what to think.

Pepper Moon's mother bowed and said, "He has behaved as one very young and foolish. But when he grows older, he will be wiser, I'm sure."

"Let it be as you wish," said Grandmother very sternly. "After all, a duck is better than a dog."

The family liked Waddle-Tail in spite of themselves. But he did try their patience. He had no sense of order whatever. And when the family sat down to dinner, Waddle-Tail behaved all the worse. He walked on the table and poked his bill into the bowl of noodles. He stepped in a dish of pink jam and knocked over four cups before Pepper Moon could take him from the table.

Grandmother set down her cup. So worn was her patience she could do nothing but rest her forehead on her hands.

"Must you have a squawking duck for a pet?" cried Pepper Moon's father. "It has no sense of order."

"I'd really like a dog!" Pepper Moon said hopefully.

"Oh, never a dog!" cried Grandmother. "Not that I dislike dogs. They are wiser than some animals. But they do not fit a house with china flowerpots."

Mother stroked Pepper Moon's hair and pushed it out of his eyes. "Go buy a bird as you have been told," she said.

So Pepper Moon left the duck with Old Tiger and hurried down Bamboo Street.

Sound the words.

roundish

Chin-shan

merchants

pigsty

trampled

demon

poetry

gardener

sprouts

A Dragon in the Garden

On the way to the bird market Pepper Moon met Bristleback. Bristleback was a roundish, black pig with a friendly tail and black, twinkling eyes. He had arrived in the city hanging upside down from a pole. The pig had wiggled and squirmed and kicked until he got the rope loose. Then, squealing, he fell at Pepper Moon's feet.

"May a demon take that pig!" cried the farmer. "He thinks himself too smart to be sold in the market."

Pepper Moon was delighted. He decided that the one pet in the world he wanted was that smart pig.

When the family saw Bristleback, they were surprised, to say the least. Pepper Moon's father and the uncles stood politely around Grandmother's tea table while she thought it over. No one in that orderly house had ever heard of a pig for a pet. They hardly knew what to think.

Pepper Moon's father bowed and said, "I know he is young and foolish. But when he grows older, he will be wiser."

"Let it be as you wish," sighed Grandmother. "A pig is surely better than a dog—
I think."

Now Bristleback had spent all his days in
a pigsty. He had no sense of order whatever.
He liked to root in the china flowerpots
and splash in the lily pool. He scratched
his back against the beautiful furniture.
But it was in the kitchen that Bristleback
behaved even worse. He chased the maids
until they scrambled up on chairs. Then he
bumped the fisherman, sending two baskets
of silvery fish flying across the kitchen.

The baskets turned upside down, and flat silvery fish covered the floor from the east wall to the west.

The cook was in such a state of shock he could not say a word. But Pepper Moon's father cried, "Bad luck has indeed fallen on our house! Must you have a pig for a pet? A pig belongs in a pigsty."

"I'd really like a puppy dog," Pepper Moon said hopefully.

"A bird would suit our family better," said his father sternly.

Pepper Moon gave the pig to Old Tiger, who promised to give him to his grandson. Then Pepper Moon ran to the bird market.

Never had he seen so many cages. They filled the shops and crowded the sidewalks. They hung in clusters along the long, narrow street. Should he buy a wise owl or a singing canary? Should he buy a sleek robin or a talking parrot? Pepper Moon did not know which to choose.

Suddenly the bird merchants moaned and started wringing their hands.

"A thousand pities!" they cried.

Down the street came an old water buffalo. He felt just as helpless and excited as the bird merchants. For every time he lifted his head, his horns caught in the bamboo cages that were hanging in clusters from the ceiling of each shop.

Pepper Moon saw in a twinkling what he had to do. He held the head of the buffalo down. And with no trouble at all he led the buffalo along the shops on the narrow street.

Old Tiger pulled his three long hairs in surprise when he saw Pepper Moon walk up with the buffalo. Then he said, "Lucky it is for you, Young Master, that everyone sleeps after teatime."

No one saw Pepper Moon lead the buffalo past the lily pool to the kitchen garden. There he tied the buffalo to a tree and gave him some bamboo sprouts to eat.

That evening the family sat in the Hall of Family Gathering and listened to Uncle Chin-shan read poetry. Suddenly there was a strange noise such as no one had ever heard before in that orderly house.

Uncle Chin-shan quietly closed the book of poetry.

"A robber!" he exclaimed.

"A witch!" cried the aunts.

"A demon!" declared Grandmother.

Pepper Moon squirmed, wanting to tell them. But he didn't have the courage.

Grandmother ordered the cook to light firecrackers in the courtyard. But when all the firecrackers had popped and banged, the queer noise came again from the far corner of the house.

Grandmother ordered the kitchen maids to beat upon the pots and pans with all their might. But when the noise stopped, again the strange sound came.

Pepper Moon was trying to get the courage to tell them it was not a robber or a witch or a demon. But just then the cook burst into the courtyard, his pigtail flying. "There is a great, roundish dragon in the kitchen garden!" he cried.

Close behind him came the gardener. "It gave a snort and stamped the ground and has horns as wide as a room!" he cried.

The women locked themselves safely in the Hall of Family Gathering. But Pepper Moon followed the men. The uncles and the cook and the gardener gathered together a mop, a sword, and some knives. Silently they crept to the kitchen garden. Then they hid behind the wall while the gardener tied a lantern on the end of a rake and pushed it through the moon gate. "Come out!" the gardener cried in a trembling voice.

There was no answer. They looked into the garden. And there among the trampled plants stood the poor trembling water buffalo, as frightened as they were.

"He's my new pet," said Pepper Moon in a very small voice.

Suddenly the men burst out laughing. They laughed so hard and so long that they could be heard even beyond the locked doors of the Hall of Family Gathering.

When Grandmother saw the kitchen garden all trampled and her bamboo sprouts eaten up, she said in a faint voice, "Perhaps a dog would be better after all."

Think about This:

1 Why do you suppose Pepper Moon bought Waddle-Tail?
2 What do you suppose Old Tiger did with all the pets Pepper Moon left with him?
3 Do you think Pepper Moon finally got a dog? Why do you think so?
4 In what ways was Pepper Moon's family different from yours?
5 How was Pepper Moon like American boys?

Dreams

Hold fast to dreams
    For if dreams die
    Life is a broken-winged bird
    That cannot fly.

    Hold fast to dreams
    For when dreams go
    Life is a barren field
    Frozen with snow.

by Langston Hughes

Beyond
the Footlights

113

Anna pulled the covers over her head and hid her face in the pillow. She rubbed her legs and sobbed. Oh, how they hurt!

The big sleeping room was dark and quiet. Long rows of beds stood against the walls. Fifty girls slept here. Like Anna, all of the girls dreamed of becoming ballerinas in the Russian Ballet. They were first-year students at the Russian Ballet School.

"I did not know learning ballet would hurt my legs and toes so much!" Anna moaned. "But it's worth it to be a ballerina! How wonderful it will be to drift like a cloud across the stage with people clapping as I dance!" With this vision Anna fell asleep, a happy smile on her face.

Next morning Anna was out of bed before sunrise. She tiptoed to the foot of her bed and grasped the bedrail. Putting her heels together, she began her exercises.

Soon Tamara woke up and rubbed her eyes. "Anna!" she whispered. "Do you never tire of practicing?"

Anna shook her head. "It's my clumsy big toe!" she whispered. "I must work harder than you learning to stand on my toes."

Suddenly a loud bell rang. There were groans as sleepy heads rose from the beds. Then fifty girls went scurrying to wash their faces in cold water.

All the girls got into line. Then each marched to a governess standing nearby with a brush. Quickly the governess brushed each girl's hair, set it in a pigtail, and tied it with a black ribbon.

Then the girls dressed, made their beds, and marched in to breakfast.

After they had eaten, lines formed again to march to the practice room.

"In line!" called Oblakov, the ballet master. "On your toes!"

Anna's toes hurt from the day before. But one lesson she had already learned was that a ballet student must master her body. Pain darted up Anna's legs as she rose to her toes. But she followed Oblakov as he led them in exercises.

"Rest now!" Oblakov called to the first-year students. "Second-year students, take your places!"

While the others rested, Anna continued exercising at the practice bar along the wall. Then she heard the headmaster call the students to attention.

"There will be a Children's Ballet next week for the Emperor and Empress," said the headmaster.

Anna wished that she might be chosen. But it was very rare for a first-year student to be permitted to dance before the Emperor and Empress.

The headmaster began reading the names. "Natasha, Manya—" The names went on. Then at the very end, Anna heard her own name called. Was it possible? She glanced at her teacher. Oblakov nodded and smiled proudly. It was true!

"It is a great honor for you to be chosen ahead of second-year students!" Oblakov exclaimed. "But you have worked very hard, little Anna."

Anna smiled proudly. She would work even harder!

All week Anna was eager to be dancing. But there were other things to be studied and other things the students must do. No one was permitted to miss the walk in the garden after lunch. A governess watched the students carefully as they walked two by two, talking quietly.

"I'd like to be practicing now!" Anna exclaimed to Tamara.

"I believe you would dance all day long!" Tamara laughed.

"Yes!" Anna laughed back. "But I also like make-up class."

On the night of the Children's Ballet, the dressing room was crowded. Anna was to be one of the dryads in the ballet. Carefully she put on the make-up that made her skin a bluish color. She drew around the corners of her eyes with a green stick. Then she began dressing in her bluish green costume, her fingers trembling.

The dryads waited for their signal to dance onto the stage. Anna stood in the wings, still trembling.

"I can't," she whispered. "I've forgotten the steps! I'll bring shame to the school!"

Then the first sounds of the ballet music started. Anna watched the older students drift like clouds onto the stage. Oblakov waved to the dryads. It was time!

Anna grasped the edges of her costume and rose on her toes. She felt the stage beneath her and caught sight of the Emperor and Empress sitting beyond the footlights. Suddenly all her fright was gone. Anna felt as light as air. For tonight her vision of dancing in a ballet was real!

The Emperor and Empress were clapping and smiling at the end of the ballet. They came behind the stage to meet the students.

Oblakov smiled. "You did well, Anna!" he exclaimed. "I am proud of you!"

The next morning Anna was up at sunrise again, practicing at the bedrail.

"Anna!" Tamara whispered. "Why are you practicing? There is no ballet today!"

"Oh, Tamara!" Anna whispered, her eyes bright. "If I am to be a great star of the ballet, I must practice!"

"That is what all of us have dreamed of," Tamara replied softly.

As Anna practiced, something seemed to cry out inside of her. "I want to become a great ballerina! I will not fail!"

Anna did not fail. She not only became one of the greatest Russian ballerinas, but she became one of the greatest ballerinas in the world. Young Anna Pavlova made her big dream come true.

Sound the words.

knife

Fung

design

toymaker

daughter

artist

describe

impossible

The Princess and the Toymaker

Long ago, in the city of Mukden in North China, there lived a prince who was loved by all his people. And the great pride of the prince's house was his little daughter, Toy Fung.

The prince's daughter had wonderful toys of almost every possible kind. There were tiny jade crickets, kites in the shape of great fierce dragons, and so many dolls that it would be impossible to describe them all. The dolls were made of glass and of ivory and of wood. Their clothes were made of fine silks with the most beautiful designs in all of Mukden.

One day Toy Fung became ill. She lay in her bed very quietly. She didn't eat, and soon she grew weak. No doctor in all of Mukden could find out what was wrong.

"Why don't you play with your dolls?" asked the prince one morning.

"They are too heavy to lift," Toy Fung said. "They were never heavy before."

The prince rushed out of Toy Fung's room and went to see the toymaker. He told him to design a doll as light as air.

"I must have it by sunset," the prince said. "My daughter is very ill. She is sad and weak. The only thing that will help her is a doll she can lift."

When the prince had gone, the toymaker tried to think of a way to design a doll that Toy Fung could lift. He pulled his ear and thought of bamboo. He scratched his head and thought of wood. Then he went to tell his son what the prince had said.

Gen Win, the toymaker's son, wanted to be an artist and not a toymaker. He had been drawing a picture in secret when his father came in and told him his problem.

As Gen Win stopped drawing, he suddenly had an idea. His heart beat higher than his father's wonderful kites had ever flown. His eyes were twinkling as bright as stars on clear winter nights.

"Bring me paper, quickly!" he called to the workers. "And paints and a thin-edged knife! I shall make the princess a whole family of dolls whose clothes have never known a needle. And Toy Fung will be able to lift them just by breathing. They shall be the pride of Toy Fung's heart."

The toymaker looked at his son. "Have you lost your mind? It is impossible to design a doll so light."

"No, it isn't impossible!" Gen Win said. Then he began to work. He painted a little girl with a pigtail. He cut her out with the thin-edged knife.

Next he painted a red coat, just the size for the girl he had drawn. He drew hands on the edges of the coat and then cut it out. He folded back the hands on the edges, so they held the coat on the doll.

"Why hands?" the old toymaker asked.

"Yes, why hands?" asked the prince, who had come quietly into the room.

"Sire," said Gen Win, "because there is not a person I know who would not give his hands to help the princess."

The prince smiled. "Come, it is sunset," he said. "We'll take it to Toy Fung."

As the prince bent over his daughter's bed, he held out the doll and said, "See, the little coat comes off."

For the first time in many days, Toy Fung smiled. She reached for the doll.

"There will be more dolls soon," Gen Win said to her. "I will make a brother for the girl and perhaps a father and mother."

"And clothes?" Toy Fung asked quickly.

"Indeed," her father said. "Gen Win, the artist, will design many clothes."

Gen Win smiled. "The artist" the prince had called him! Perhaps he would be allowed to be a real artist, not just a toymaker who only drew designs for toys.

"Gen Win," said the prince, "because of you, the princess is better already. I am going to hire a teacher for you. When you are older, you will be the greatest artist in my kingdom."

From that day on, Toy Fung grew better. And after many years and much hard work, Gen Win did become a great artist.

Sound the words.

molded

robot

lifelike

designers

Paris

fashion

success

entertain

popular

Sight words.

mannequins   characters

Dolls of Many Faces

In almost all countries children play with dolls. They walk their dolls and talk to them. They give their dolls a bath, wash and set their hair, and dress them in all kinds of clothes. But did you know that people have used dolls for many things besides toys?

The first dolls were probably bits of wood or stone that had accidentally formed into the shape of a person. It is thought they were found by early man and became important to him because they looked something like himself. Children were never allowed to play with these dolls. People thought they were magic and had the power to bring good health to a sick person, good crops, and success in war. Some dolls were even used as magic to keep rain clouds and insects away.

Long ago people began to make life-size dolls out of stone, wood, or metal to honor famous people. We call them statues. Did you know that statues are also dolls?

Another kind of life-size doll to honor a great person was made of wax. Collections of life-size wax dolls have been made of famous people. The wax dolls are so life-like they are spooky. You can see these dolls on display in wax museums. They are very popular.

Mannequins are still another kind of life-size doll. Mannequins are used with success by tailors to make their clothes fit people well. And you can see new clothes on life-like mannequins in many store windows that you pass by.

Long ago the clothes designers of Paris sent life-size dolls to important people all over the world. These dolls were called fashion dolls. The designers sent them to show people the latest designs in clothes. Paris fashion dolls were molded in wax and were dressed in clothes of real cloth, so they looked almost like people. But they could not move or talk.

Puppets were the first dolls that could be made to move and talk. They were used to act out plays to entertain people.

The very first puppets were probably hand puppets. A man gave each puppet its voice and its movement. But since one man has only two hands, plays acted out by hand puppets could only have two characters on the stage at a time. Moving puppets with strings solved this problem and brought more lifelike movement. Some of the greatest of all plays have been acted out with puppets. Perhaps you know of some puppet characters who have become popular.

Today there is still a new kind of doll— the robot. Robots are already used as toys. There are life-size robots, too. What do you think people will find to do with these new life-size dolls?

Sound the words.

doorway

enjoy

selfish

Fatima

Mustapha

Hodja

Ahmet

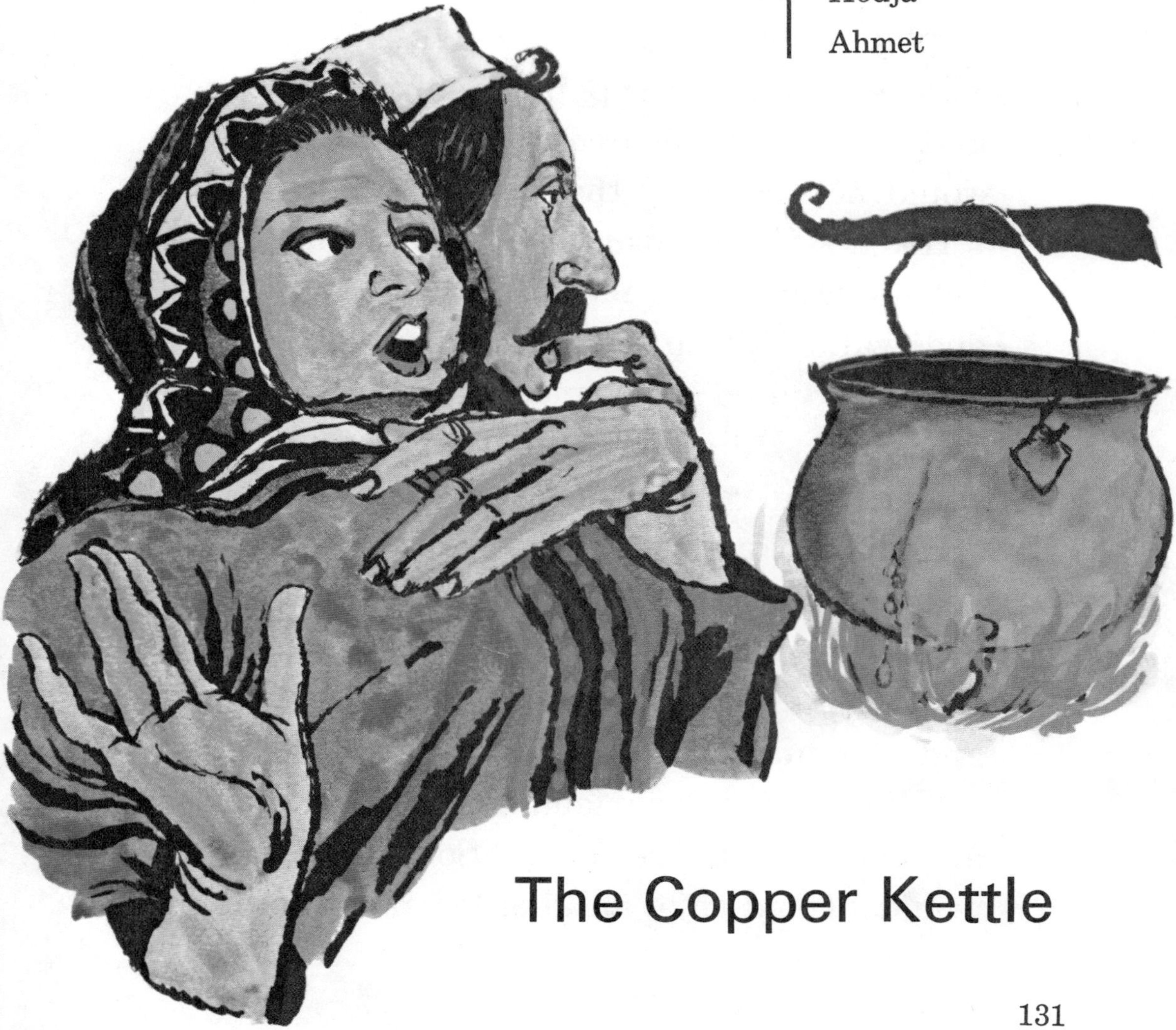

Sight words.

doubt   Ali's

The Copper Kettle

A leak in the kettle!" cried Fatima as she waved her arms excitedly. "The soup is dripping into the fire!"

Hodja wasn't always alarmed by his wife's wailing. But this was a special sort of trouble. A leaky kettle meant no dinner—a problem worth a man's attention.

"Yes, it has a leak!" cried Hodja as he watched the soup dripping from the copper kettle into the charcoal fire. The soup would not last long that way.

Hodja was not usually a man of action, but he became one now. He left his house and walked down the cobbled street.

Hodja peered at Ahmet, standing in his doorway. He owed Ahmet a measure of wheat. So he couldn't ask him for a kettle.

Hodja looked at Ali's door and shook his head. Ali's wife had a sharp tongue.

He looked at Mustapha's door and nodded. At Hodja's knock the door slowly opened, and the hungry Hodja shuffled inside.

"Welcome, good friend!" said Mustapha, always happy to see Hodja. Some days they would sit and enjoy talking for many hours.

But if Mustapha was expecting a long talk today, he was disappointed.

"Our soup! Save our soup!" cried Hodja, waving his arms. It was clear to Mustapha that quick action was needed.

"Gladly, good friend," said Mustapha.

"You can loan us a kettle for a few days while ours is being mended," said Hodja, "and all will be well, true friend. I shall not forget how thoughtful you are."

Now Mustapha was not at all pleased to loan his kettle, nor was his wife pleased a tiny bit. But he couldn't go back on his promise. There was nothing to do but bring in a kettle and loan it to Hodja.

"Thank you—a thousand thanks," Hodja said. He shuffled home with the big copper kettle in time to save at least half of the good bean soup.

A few days later, Hodja's kettle had been mended. With twinkling eyes he went to return Mustapha's property. Mustapha was happy to have his big copper kettle home again. His wife had given him no peace, saying they would never see it again.

"But what is this?" Mustapha said as he peered inside the kettle.

"That is a dear little baby kettle, born to the big kettle when it was at our house," said Hodja, smiling.

Mustapha gulped. But, after all, a shiny little copper kettle was good to have.

"How nice," Mustapha said, trying to act as if he saw nothing queer about the birth of a baby kettle.

A week later Fatima began wailing over another leak in the mended kettle. It was Hodja's favorite goat's milk soup now dripping into the charcoal fire. And Hodja knew just what to do. He rushed to Mustapha's house and asked for the kettle.

"Gladly, gladly," said Mustapha. "My big kettle is yours anytime you wish it."

And Mustapha's wife, who had been selfish before, came running with the kettle in her hand, eager to loan it to Hodja.

The days went by. Mustapha and his wife wondered if the big kettle would have twin kettles this time. At last Mustapha heard Hodja as he shuffled up the steps.

"Welcome, my good friend, welcome," Mustapha said with a smile. But he couldn't keep his eyes away from Hodja's empty hands. Then Mustapha looked at Hodja's face, wet with streams of tears.

"It is bad news I bring, dear friend," sighed Hodja. "Your kettle, your beautiful copper kettle—it is dead."

"Dead!" roared Mustapha.

"Yes, dead," said Hodja sadly.

"Who ever heard of a kettle dying?" cried Mustapha in an angry voice.

"Whatever is able to give birth is also able to die," replied Hodja. "You didn't doubt that the little kettle was born to your big kettle. How can you doubt me when I tell you about the big kettle dying? Oh, poor copper kettle!"

Mustapha was still standing in his door-way with empty hands as Hodja shuffled home to enjoy a bowl of the soup that was cooking in the big copper kettle.

Sound the words.

share
storms
shore
ermine
driftwood
surf
Iomea
dunes
Eskimo
igloos

Sight words.

southward   calm

Konok's Trade

Neeluk had been waiting eagerly for the whaling ships to stop at his Eskimo village to trade. He had waited and waited. But then the storms began, and he knew he would have to wait a little longer. The surf came rolling in over the shore, breaking on the sand dunes near the igloos. It seemed a long time before the storms were over.

"Do you think the whaling ships will come now?" asked Neeluk's friend Iomea when at last the sea was calm again.

"I hope so," replied Neeluk. "I've been waiting to trade my ermine skin and get some chewing gum."

"The ships are not stopping! They are passing the village!" called one of the men. "See, they go southward."

Neeluk's mother and sister came running from the tent. "Mother, will all the ships go southward without stopping, even if the sea is calm?" Neeluk asked.

"Yes," she answered. "They must get out of these icy waters before the ice becomes too thick and catches them."

"Now I won't be able to trade my ermine skin," said Neeluk.

"Next spring you can trade it," said his mother. "Have patience, son. Storms cause bad things, but they bring us good things, too. See the driftwood in the surf? You know we are in great need of it. And there will be many clams on shore when the tide goes out."

"Perhaps there will even be crabs," said Konok, Neeluk's sister.

"Crab meat tastes good. But gum is what I really want," said Neeluk.

Next morning, when Neeluk and Konok woke up, most of the people had already left their igloos and tents. They were on the beach getting logs out of the icy waters and rolling them up on shore.

Some of the Eskimo children already had their wooden pans and were gathering clams on the sand dunes. Neeluk and Konok got their pans and ran to make their catches before the clams were all gone.

Suddenly Konok gave a glad cry. "Look!" she exclaimed. "I found a big crab!"

Neeluk felt better. It wasn't gum, but he did like crab meat. And he knew that Konok would share her crab with him. So he took his pan and ran to another place on the beach to gather clams.

With her friend Woodlet, Konok continued searching in the sand dunes. But Woodlet kept looking at the crab. At last she said, "Konok, if you give me your crab, I'll give you my bracelet."

"But Neeluk and I want to eat the crab," Konok told her friend.

"It's a pretty bracelet," Woodlet said. She offered Konok the red and white beads, then slipped them on Konok's wrist.

"I'll trade," Konok finally said. "Maybe I'll find another crab."

Konok found many clams, but she didn't find another crab. Then Neeluk and Iomea came running up to her. "Iomea wants to see the crab," Neeluk said.

"I don't have it any more," Konok told him. "I traded it."

"What for?" he cried.

"For this bracelet," Konok said as she held out her arm.

Now Neeluk didn't have any gum, and he wouldn't have crab meat either. He looked so disappointed that Konok wished she had kept the crab to share with him.

"I'll look for another crab after I take these clams to the tent," she told him.

When Konok returned to the beach, her mother and father had just rolled a log up from the water, and her father had put his mark on it. Konok saw that it was a spruce log. So she looked inside. If she found what she was looking for, Neeluk would not be so unhappy. There it was!

"Now I've got a secret and a bracelet," she said happily as she felt her wrist.

The bracelet was gone! Konok searched all along the beach and among the driftwood, but she couldn't find it.

"What are you looking for?" asked Neeluk, coming up behind her.

"For my new bracelet," Konok answered. "It was too big, and it slipped off. Will you and your friends help me find it?"

But the boys did not want to look for the bracelet.

"If you help find my bracelet, I'll tell you my secret," offered Konok.

"What secret?" Neeluk asked.

"It wouldn't be a secret if I told," said Konok. "But it's a good secret."

"Is it good to eat?" asked Neeluk.

"It tastes good," Konok said.

So Neeluk and his friends began searching for the bracelet. "Did you look inside the tent?" Neeluk asked Konok.

"Yes," Konok answered, "but I couldn't find it there."

"I'll look again," Neeluk told her.

While Neeluk was searching the tent, he got hungry. "I think I'll have some fish," he thought. He went to the food box to get a piece of dried fish. There in one corner were the red and white beads! Konok had helped herself to dried fish when she had brought up the last pan of clams.

Konok was delighted when Neeluk gave her the bracelet.

"Now where's your secret?" Neeluk asked. His friends waited eagerly.

"Come. I'll show you," Konok replied as she led them to the log. "See," she said. "It's a spruce log. It has gum."

"Spruce gum!" the boys cried happily.

"I like spruce gum better than the kind traded on ships!" Neeluk said.

The boys took out their knives and began to dig the gum out of the log.

"Now we are both happy," said Konok. "You have your chewing gum, and I have my pretty bracelet."

Sound the words.

fearful

buyer

Kimba

awakened

Ohalla

bargained

businessman

thieving

flung

Swahili Drumbeat

145

A young Swahili boy named Kimba walked along behind his father on the jungle trail to the city. Like his father, Kimba carried a load on his head.

The big reed basket on Kimba's head held twenty-two crows' eggs. "When I get to the city, I'll sell these eggs for five pennies apiece," Kimba said to himself. "I'll be rich. What a gift I'll be able to buy for my chief!"

Kimba's father, Ohalla, carried a spear in his hand. On his head he carried a box filled with little animal figures carved out of wood. He would sell these to a buyer in a small shop in the city.

A brisk jungle breeze swept across the trail. Elephant grass rustled, and palm trees shook their leaves.

Puff! Blow! A gust of wind set Kimba's basket to rocking gently on his head. He stopped and held his breath. "What if the basket blows off?" he said to himself. But Kimba never thought of taking the basket off his head, no matter how much he cared for the eggs. His people never carried anything anywhere except on their heads.

Kimba had stopped when the brisk breeze wobbled his basket. Now his father was far ahead, almost out of sight. Kimba hurried after him and had almost caught up when he stopped and gasped. This time it wasn't a sudden breeze that made him stop. Something up ahead rustled in the tangled grass. And something that looked like a long, thick rope came creeping out. A snake!

"It's creeping up on Father!" thought Kimba.

If he called and his father turned, the snake would strike. He must do something! There was no time to set the basket down, but Kimba no longer cared about the eggs. He watched the snake, its tongue darting this way and that. The snake's ugly head was moving closer and closer to Father.

Kimba knelt and pulled at a big rock. The basket on his head wobbled. Standing up, he lifted the heavy rock in both hands. Carefully he aimed the rock. Then he flung it straight at the snake!

Kimba shut his eyes tightly, fearful that he had missed the snake. For a long moment he dared not open his eyes. Then he heard it—a voice! Still fearful, he opened first one eye and then the other.

Ohalla came hurrying back down the trail, his spear held ready. "What is it, Kimba? What has happened?"

Kimba pointed at the snake, lying crushed beneath the rock. And now that Father was safe, Kimba's thoughts turned to the eggs.

He reached a hand up to his head. The reed basket was gone!

"All that work for nothing!" Kimba said. Then he began looking for the basket. It was lying in the tall, thick elephant grass, and so were the eggs.

"Father, look!" cried Kimba. "I dropped twenty-two eggs, and only two are smashed. You are safe, and so are the eggs!"

Ohalla smiled and laid a hand on Kimba's shoulder. "We've both had good fortune," he said. "I am especially lucky to have such a warrior for a son."

Kimba's heart began to swell. Warrior! His father had called him a warrior. Kimba could not have felt as proud if he had been made chief of the village.

After that, Kimba and his father were on the lookout for any new sign of danger. But nothing else happened, and soon they came to the city.

Kimba's father headed for the shop where he sold his carved animal figures. Kimba headed for the town offices.

Now that he was no longer on the tangled jungle trail but on the smooth streets of the city, Kimba could almost run with the egg basket on his head. Soon he arrived at the offices. They were in a bamboo house with a flag flying above. Kimba knocked. A bearded man opened the door.

"The drums have told that you buy crows and their eggs," Kimba said.

"That's true," the man replied. "We wish to kill the thieving crows so your people will have more food and grain. I'm busy now, but if you'll wait here, I'll pay you for your eggs when I have finished."

The Swahili boy sat down on the porch steps with the basket beside him. The warm sunshine soon put him fast asleep. Much later a strange noise awakened him.

Kimba knelt beside his basket and blinked at what he saw. Then he gasped and jumped to his feet. His wonderful, smooth eggs! They were no longer eggs. They had hatched into baby crows!

Just then the bearded man walked out on the porch. "Ah, there you are. Well, let's see how many eggs you have."

Kimba said, "I have eggs no longer. See, they are birds now. The drums have told that you will pay twenty-five pennies for each crow. Is that so?"

"Well, yes," the man said, rubbing his chin. "But now see here. These birds don't even have their feathers. They were eggs when you first showed them to me."

"Yes," said Kimba, "but you were busy then and did not buy them." Kimba felt like a real businessman. He was doing business just as his father did when he bargained for the price of his wooden figures.

The bearded man began to laugh. "I never thought I'd see the day when a boy would out-bargain me. But very well, twenty-five pennies apiece it is. But mind you, no one will receive more than five pennies again for a bird without feathers," he said.

Kimba grinned his biggest grin and held out his hand for the money. The buyer kept dropping money into his hand until Kimba thought he had a fortune.

"What a day!" Kimba thought. He had saved his father's life and had been called a warrior. He had bargained just like a full-grown businessman. And now he had enough money to buy a gift for his chief and still have some left for himself.

Just then a crow flew above the offices, darting about the flag. Kimba flung his hand toward the bird and shouted happily, "You have been very bad, O Thieving One, but not today. Thank you. Thank you for a wonderful day!"

Think about This:

1 Where do Swahili people live?
2 At one point in the story, why did Kimba no longer care about the eggs?
3 Why was the bearded man willing to pay for crows and crows' eggs?
4 Why do you suppose the bearded man warned Kimba that no one would receive more than five pennies again for a bird without feathers?
5 What did Kimba mean when he said, "The drums have told that you buy crows and their eggs"?

Sound the words.

shoulders
Andrews
flattered
thumb
Thaddeus
crayons

Song of
the Empty Bottles

155

All but Thaddeus

Thaddeus went to the Neighborhood House after school whenever he felt like it—to draw with crayons or finger paints, play ping-pong, and have fun. Some days he felt like it, and some days he did not. But he never missed going on Thursday, because on that afternoon Mr. Andrews came to sing songs with his guitar.

Some of the songs were happy and some were sad, and the children all sang along with Mr. Andrews—all except Thaddeus. He made his mouth go, but he did not sing out loud because he would rather listen. He did not want to miss hearing one single boom of Mr. Andrews' deep voice or a pling-plung of his guitar. Instead, he waited until he was alone. Then he sang by himself.

Sometimes when he sang, Thaddeus thought of songs he had never heard before.

My mamma goes away all day,

My mamma goes away all day,

My mamma goes away all day.

Then Thaddeus wished, more than he wished for anything else in the world, that he had a guitar. With a guitar he could make the wonderful pling-plung sounds to go along with his singing, the way Mr. Andrews did. If he had a guitar, he would let his voice boom, too.

One day when all the children had crowded around, Mr. Andrews said, "The boy in the back there, I don't know your name."

The other children looked at Thaddeus, and Thaddeus looked behind him, to see whom Mr. Andrews was talking to.

"I mean you, young fellow," Mr. Andrews said, looking right at Thaddeus. "Come inside the circle. I want to talk to you."

Thaddeus felt hot and cold and afraid. He loved Mr. Andrews, but he had never dared go and talk to him and lean against him, as some of the others did. But now the circle opened in front of him, and slowly he came near.

"What's your name?" Mr. Andrews said.

Thaddeus put his head down and said in a soft voice, "Thaddeus."

"I didn't hear that," Mr. Andrews said.

"Thaddeus!" the other children screamed. "His name is Thaddeus!"

"I want to hear it from this young man himself," and Mr. Andrews put his arm around Thaddeus' shoulders.

Then Thaddeus spoke right up and said, "Thaddeus."

"Will you tell me why you make believe you are singing in the back there, when you're really not singing at all?"

"I like to hear you sing," Thaddeus said. "And if I sing, then I can't hear you."

Mr. Andrews looked surprised and tried not to smile. "Well, I am flattered," he said, "but you would have fun singing along with the others if you tried it."

"I have fun hearing," said Thaddeus. "I sing when I'm by myself."

The other children had begun to drift away, to go back to their crayons and their playing. And after a while only Thaddeus was there with Mr. Andrews. Suddenly he reached out and touched the strings of Mr. Andrews' guitar with his thumb.

"Here, hold it," Mr. Andrews said, and he reached over Thaddeus' shoulders and put the guitar in his arms in just the right way. Thaddeus drew his thumb across the strings four times. Each time he could feel the whole guitar tremble in his arms, and he could hear the strings ring in his ears like a million bells. He said very softly, "How much is a guitar?"

"This one cost a great deal—a hundred dollars. Why do you want to know?"

"I want a guitar," Thaddeus said.

"But you don't know how to play one."

"I could learn."

Mr. Andrews looked hard at Thaddeus. At last he said, "I just happen to know someone who has a very nice guitar that he will sell for fifteen dollars. Do you suppose you could get fifteen dollars to buy a guitar?"

"I don't know," Thaddeus said. He got up and walked quickly out of the Neighborhood House, straight up the hill and home. There he waited for his mother to come from work.

Sound the words.

collect
Bernadine
errands
banty
shredding
factory

To Buy a Guitar

Thaddeus sat on the front steps waiting for his mother to come home. As he waited, his little sister came over to him.

"What have you got inside you?" asked Bernadine. Even when Thaddeus was only sitting quietly, his sister always could tell when he had something on his mind.

162

"Nothing much," Thaddeus said.

"Tell me."

"I want to buy a guitar," he said.

"Will you let me play it?" questioned Bernadine.

"Sometimes, if you're very careful."

"I'll be careful," Bernadine said.

After a while their mother came up the hill and turned in at the little iron gate. She sat down on the front steps to catch her breath.

"Have you children been good today?" she asked.

"Yes," Bernadine said. "Thaddeus wants to buy a guitar."

163

"A guitar! Whatever do you want with a guitar?" asked Mother.

"I want to play it and sing with it."

"That's for big kids," said Mother. "You are too small to play a guitar."

"Can he?" Bernadine asked, following her mother into the house.

"Can he what?"

"Can he get a guitar?" said Bernadine.

"How much is a guitar?" asked Mother.

"A hundred dollars," Thaddeus said.

"Are you out of your mind, boy?"

"But I can get one for fifteen dollars."

"Oh, that's different," his mother said. "No problem at all. You just go out in the yard and water the little banty tree every day for a week, and it will start growing dollar bills and quarters and dimes and nickels. Then you can pick them off and go downtown and buy anything you like. And while you're down there, would you mind buying me a dress and some shoes?"

Thaddeus knew this was her way of saying they did not have fifteen dollars for a guitar. Not now. Or any other time.

The next Thursday, after singing time, Thaddeus told Mr. Andrews how much he still wanted the guitar.

"Did you ever think of trying to earn some money?" Mr. Andrews asked.

"How could I earn some money?"

"Running errands," Mr. Andrews suggested. "Doing chores for people. Nickels soon add up to dollar bills, you know."

"People in my neighborhood don't have any more money than my mamma," Thaddeus said. "They do their own chores and run their own errands."

"Yes," said Mr. Andrews. "Of course."

"I do earn money sometimes," Thaddeus said. "But only a little bit. Enough to buy an ice-cream cone or a bottle of soda."

"How do you earn that money?"

"I collect empty bottles and take them back to the store. I collect old newspapers and take them to the shredding factory. I get ten cents for a wagonload."

"Do you have a wagon?"

"An old rickety wagon," said Thaddeus.

"Well, if you collect enough wagonloads for the shredding factory and find enough bottles, and if you don't spend the money for soda, pretty soon you'll have enough to buy your guitar."

"How soon?"

"If you start right away, maybe you can earn the money by the Fourth of July— that's about three months."

"I wish it was July right now," Thaddeus said.

"Then you wouldn't have anything to look forward to."

"I would have the guitar."

"You win," said Mr. Andrews. "But for now, start to work so that you'll have the money in July."

"Okay," Thaddeus said.

Sound the words.

Eaton

Embassy

refund

Cambridge

incinerator

superintendents

hydrant

there've

discouraged

Sight word.

chord

Secret in a Jar

The next Thursday Mr. Andrews said to Thaddeus, "While you're earning money, I'll teach you a little about how to play the guitar. We can use mine."

Mr. Andrews showed Thaddeus how to rest the guitar on his lap, with the fingers of his left hand pressing on the strings and the fingers of his right hand plunking them.

At first, pressing down on the strings cut his fingers. And sometimes it was hard to remember where to put his fingers for the sound he wanted. Often he made mistakes, and harsh sounds came from the strings.

But Thaddeus did not get discouraged, and every week, after the other children went home, Mr. Andrews gave him a lesson.

In time, Thaddeus learned six different ways to put his fingers down on the strings to make six different chords. Each chord sounded different from all the others, and he loved every one of them. His plunking no longer made harsh sounds. And no matter what note he sang, he could always find a chord on the guitar that made his song even more beautiful.

More than ever before Thaddeus found himself making up songs as he practiced on Mr. Andrews' guitar.

It's a hot day, Mr. Fireman.
Please open the fire hydrant for us.

It's a hot day, Mr. Fireman.
Please open the fire hydrant for us.

"That's a nice song," Mr. Andrews said when Thaddeus sang it. "Perhaps someday you'll make up a longer one."

Thaddeus thought about that for a while. Then he said, "Yes, maybe I will."

Collecting bottles and newspapers was not as much fun as learning to play the guitar. No matter where he went, Thaddeus kept his eyes open for empty bottles. He found them in parking lots and in gutters and in trash cans, where people had dumped them. He found them in alleys and beside park benches. It was hard, slow work, and often he felt very discouraged.

But then Thaddeus discovered the tall apartment buildings that began a few blocks from his house. He heard that the people who lived in these buildings left their empty bottles in incinerator closets on every floor. They left their old newspapers there, too.

He asked the building superintendents if he could have the bottles and newspapers. Some superintendents said he couldn't. But some said he could. So he no longer had to go to alleys and park benches, gutters and parking lots to find bottles.

With his rickety wagon he collected the bottles from the incinerator closets and carted them to the grocery store. There he got refund money for them. He took the newspapers to a shredding factory on the street behind his house.

He collected every day after school and on Saturdays and Sundays, and he saved the money he earned. He kept it in a peanut butter jar and didn't tell anyone about it, not even Bernadine.

Every few days Thaddeus dumped his money out on his bed to see how much he had. The pile of nickels and dimes grew very slowly. After eight weeks he only had four dollars and seventy-one cents—it would take him forever to save fifteen dollars.

But then he thought about the guitar. So he put the money back in the peanut butter jar and went out and carted more bottles to earn more refund money.

Then one Sunday afternoon, as usual, he went to the Oxford House, which was ten stories tall. Every Sunday, for the past eight weeks, he had taken the elevator to the tenth floor and looked in the closet. He would look in the closet on every floor, right down to the ground. He did the same thing in every apartment building in the neighborhood.

This Sunday afternoon the doorman at the Oxford House wouldn't let him in. "Can't have you in the building," he said.

Thaddeus left and went to the Cambridge House. The same thing happened there. "No boys allowed inside," the Cambridge doorman said. "Go away."

It was the same at Eaton House, Rugby House, Wiltshire Apartments, and Hampshire House. "Go away. No boys allowed." That was the story everywhere.

At Embassy Gardens the doorman said, "Sorry, young fellow. Can't let you in."

"Why not?"

"There've been some robberies here."

"But I'm not a robber," said Thaddeus.

"I know you're not. All the same, those are my orders. Sorry." Then a lady came out of the Embassy Gardens, and the doorman blew his whistle for a taxi.

Thaddeus walked away.

Think about This:

1 Do you think that Mr. Andrews really knew about the people in Thaddeus' neighborhood? Why?
2 Now that Thaddeus cannot go into the apartment buildings, how do you suppose he will earn money to buy the guitar?

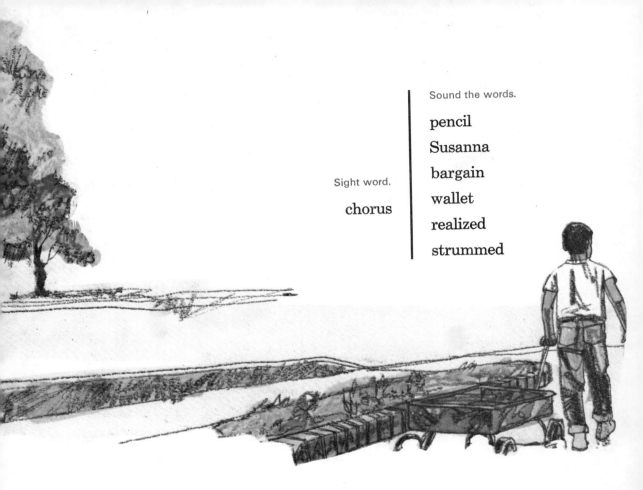

Sound the words.

pencil
Susanna
bargain
wallet
realized
strummed

Sight word.

chorus

Bottles in the Dark

The next Thursday Thaddeus went to the Neighborhood House. At the end of the singing, he started to leave with the others, but Mr. Andrews stopped him. "Aren't you going to take your lesson today?"

"I don't feel like it," Thaddeus said.

"Why not?" said Mr. Andrews. "What's the matter?"

175

"Nothing much," said Thaddeus.

"Come on, now. Tell me. I want to know."

So Thaddeus said, "I can't get any more bottles from the apartment houses. They won't let me in. Now I don't think I can ever find enough bottles to save up fifteen dollars."

Mr. Andrews didn't say anything. He just strummed quietly on his guitar. Thaddeus could see that he was thinking.

Finally Mr. Andrews said, "You don't care much about collecting bottles, do you?"

"No, I don't care much about it at all."

"What do you like to do?" Mr. Andrews asked.

"I like to make songs and sing them."

"That's what I thought. But you've never really made up a whole song, have you? Like 'Blue Tail Fly' or 'Oh! Susanna.' "

"I guess not," said Thaddeus.

"Why don't you try?" said Mr. Andrews. "Whenever I hear a new song, I get out a pad and pencil and write it down. Then I can save it and sing it whenever I want to. Here's what I'll do. If you make up a song that I like, I'll pay you ten dollars for it. Then with only a few more bottles or a few more newspapers you will have enough money to buy the guitar and still have a few dollars left. Is that a bargain?"

Thaddeus could hardly believe it. Ten dollars just for a song! It would take five hundred bottles to get ten dollars. And a ton of newspapers to get nine dollars.

A song was something you couldn't see or touch. How could it be worth ten dollars? Well, if Mr. Andrews said so, then it must be so. Thaddeus walked home thinking that he would make up a song that very night, after he went to bed.

Up until now, whenever Thaddeus made up bits of a song, he did it without trying. It just came to him. He might be walking down the street and see something and make up a song about it. But, when he went to bed and tried to make one up, no song came.

No matter how hard Thaddeus tried—day or night, walking, running, standing still, or lying down—no new song came to him. What he thought, at first, was going to be a quick way of earning ten dollars was turning out to be very hard. Maybe handling a ton of newspapers or collecting old bottles was an easier way of earning the money. Maybe making up a whole song for the rest of the guitar money wouldn't be a bargain after all.

So, once again, he began to keep a sharp lookout for bottles. He had only collected a few when he suddenly realized that he was singing, making up a new song—a song about empty bottles. The words and the notes came to him in bits and pieces.

The first part of the song came to him when he saw three bottles high on a wall.

He had to wait for a tall boy to come along and get them down for him. "I saw three bottles on a high wall. I wished that I was six feet tall." Thaddeus thought maybe he could put that in a song.

Another time, he put nine bottles on the kitchen table and tapped them with a spoon. Each bottle made a different sound, and Thaddeus discovered that he could play a tune on them. This gave him an idea for still another verse. "I tapped some bottles with my spoon and got this funny little tune." Suddenly he realized that making up a song wasn't so hard, after all.

Then he remembered that the songs sung by Mr. Andrews had a chorus that came after each verse. What could his chorus be about? Thaddeus thought, "I can even find bottles in the dark," and then he thought, "That could be the chorus. 'Bottles in the alley, bottles in the park. If there is a bottle, I can find it in the dark.' "

As Thaddeus continued to look for bottles, he thought of more verses for his song. Some were good, and he remembered them and put them in. Others he decided were not as good, and he just forgot them.

At last he thought that his song was long enough. When Thursday came, he took his money jar and went to Neighborhood House. After the other children had gone, Thaddeus picked up Mr. Andrews' guitar and sang his song and strummed the chords to go with it. He made his voice bounce and float along, high and sweet.

I look for bottles ev'rywhere,
Where I find them I don't care.

Bottles in the alley, bottles in the park,
If there is a bottle, I can find it in the dark.

I saw three bottles on a high wall,
I wished that I was six feet tall.

Bottles in the alley, bottles in the park,
If there is a bottle, I can find it in the dark.

I tapped some bottles with my spoon
And got this funny little tune.

Bottles in the alley, bottles in the park,
If there is a bottle, I can find it in the dark.

I saw a bottle in the lake,
Reached it with a big, long rake.

Bottles in the alley, bottles in the park,
If there is a bottle, I can find it in the dark.

After the first time, Mr. Andrews sang along on the chorus. Thaddeus could tell that Mr. Andrews liked the song, and he was not surprised. He liked the song himself.

Then Mr. Andrews asked Thaddeus to sing it again. He took out a pad and pencil and wrote down the words and drew some lines and marked down some notes. "All it needs now is a name," Mr. Andrews said. "How do you like 'The Empty Bottle Song'?"

"I like that fine," Thaddeus said, and Mr. Andrews took his pencil and wrote it down at the top of the pad.

"Thank you for the song," Mr. Andrews said. Then he took ten one-dollar bills out of his wallet and handed them to Thaddeus.

"Just a minute. The guitar is in my car," Mr. Andrews said, and he went outside.

Thaddeus emptied his jar of money on a chair, counted out five dollars, and put it with the ten one-dollar bills Mr. Andrews had given him.

Now Mr. Andrews brought the guitar in, handling it with great care, and polished it up a little with his handkerchief.

Thaddeus could hardly wait to hold it. "Here's the fifteen dollars," he said.

"Thank you," said Mr. Andrews, putting the fifteen dollars in his wallet. "Here is your guitar," and he handed it to Thaddeus. How cool and smooth it felt, and it shone like a mirror. And when Thaddeus drew his right thumb softly across the strings, the guitar trembled. It was smaller and lighter than Mr. Andrews' guitar but just the right size for a boy. It did not have such a loud voice either, but it had a sweet voice. Thaddeus thought it was the sweetest sound he had ever heard.

Sound the words.

scrawny

grapes

cornflakes

brand-new

Moses

stoops

where'd

Singalong

Thaddeus carried his guitar home more carefully than he would have carried half a dozen eggs. He walked fast, but he didn't run, and he picked his feet up at curbs so that he wouldn't trip. There at last was the iron gate to his yard, and the scrawny little banty tree, the front stoop, the front door.

185

Thaddeus set his guitar on the kitchen table. He got a glass of water and drank it. Then he got another and poured it on the banty tree. How did he know? Maybe the poor little thing was thirsty.

Then he sat down on the front porch with his guitar and began to sing and play. He played "Blue Tail Fly," and he played "Oh! Susanna," and he played "Go Down Moses."

Pretty soon some people across the street were sitting in their windows and on their stoops. Everybody was catching on and singing along with him.

When Bernadine came home, she stopped outside the gate for just a minute, then came in and sat down next to her brother.

It was getting close to six o'clock. Any minute now their mother would be coming up the hill from work, out of breath and tired. Thaddeus was playing a song the neighbors didn't know, but they were catching on when he sang the chorus.

Bottles in the alley, bottles in the park,
If there is a bottle, I can find it in the dark.

Thaddeus was singing a verse of the song as his mother reached the gate. She stood there listening.

I saw a bottle in the lake,
Reached it with a big, long rake.

Then everybody joined in.

Bottles in the alley, bottles in the park,
If there is a bottle, I can find it in the dark.

That was the end of the song. Thaddeus' mother came through the gate.

"What are we going to have for supper?" asked Thaddeus.

"Son, I see you got the guitar after all."

"Yes, Mamma."

"Where'd you get the money to buy it?"

Thaddeus almost said, "I picked it off the banty tree, Mamma." But he didn't say it. He said, "Some of it I earned collecting wagonloads of bottles and papers. And some of it Mr. Andrews paid me for making up a song."

"Well, all I can say is you're going to come to a good end or a bad end. I don't know which. You mark my words. Now you go right on singing. I'll listen from inside. I'm going to fix some supper."

Thaddeus drew his thumb over the strings three times and began to sing again. But this time he strummed a brand-new song. He had begun to smell the dinner his mother was cooking, and it was making him very hungry—so hungry that his new song was all about food.

Pancakes, cornflakes, squash, and cherries,
Pickles, lemons, beans, and berries.

This is the food I love to eat.
I don't care if it's sour or sweet.

Grapes and apples, bread and honey,
Stew and chicken, chocolate money.

This is the food I love to eat.
I don't care if it's sour or sweet.

His mother was calling him now. After
dinner he would make up more words for
the new song. Then he could sing it for
Mr. Andrews on Thursday.

Think about This:

1 Why do you suppose Mother told Thaddeus he
   was going to come to a good end or bad end?
2 Why do you suppose Mr. Andrews offered
   Thaddeus ten dollars for something that he could
   not see or touch?
3 Thaddeus made up songs about the things around
   him. See if you can make up the same kind of song.

City Child

The sidewalk is my yard,
  The lamppost is my tree;
Up three long flights of stairs,
  My home is Flat 4C.

The fire escape my porch,
  Where clothes hang out to dry;
All day the noise and rush,
  All night the trains go by.

Tall buildings all around
  Reach up and shadow me;
Sometimes the great big sun
  Comes peeping round to see.

All day the people pass,
  They hurry as they go;
But when they are my friends,
  They stop and say hello.

by Lois Lenski

Sound the words.

mask

microscope

scoop

flippers

contrast

future

weird

desert

explored

gear

recreation

Sight words.

ocean   awe

Answers from the Sea

193

Imagine that you are walking along the edge of the sea on a bright summer day. The waves come rolling in and break gently at your feet. As far as the eye can see, miles of blue water stretch out beneath the sun and seem to touch the sky.

How empty and lifeless the sea looks on such a day! And above all, how peaceful. But the sea is not empty, nor is it lifeless. And seldom is it peaceful. When big storms stir up the sea, mighty ships may be smashed by the toss of one giant wave. And the deeps of the sea are so full of life that, by contrast, the land seems almost like a desert.

Scoop up a handful of salty sea water. What do you see? Probably nothing but clear water. Yet, if you had a microscope, that handful of salty water would appear as it really is—a jungle in which millions of strange creatures are at battle to stay alive. Under a microscope some plants and animals living in the oceans of our own world appear more weird than any creatures you could imagine from outer space.

The sea itself is a contrast. It holds not only the smallest but also the largest of living things. We sometimes look in awe at pictures of giant dinosaurs that walked the earth long ago. Some of the largest dinosaurs weighed thirty tons. The ground must have trembled beneath their footsteps. But if we saw the blue whale, which is in the ocean today, we would be struck with even greater awe. For it is five times as heavy as the largest of dinosaurs.

There are many other huge creatures in the sea that must weigh several tons—some we have discovered. Others are still not known. A thousand years from now, when we have explored many strange places in space, we may still be finding weird creatures far down in the ocean deeps.

There is a very good reason why we need to explore the sea. We are quickly using up the coal, oil, and other important minerals of the world. Copper may one day become as rare and valuable a metal as silver. The land may truly become a desert of waste. But in and under the ocean there are enough minerals to supply our needs for a million years. Man has already begun "mining the ocean." Much of the metal used in making the body of a modern airplane comes from seawater.

It is in the sea that we may find the answer to man's greatest problem. Today a third of the people on earth do not get enough food. Yet every day thousands of new babies come into the world.

How are we going to feed the new millions of tomorrow? It seems more and more likely that the answer will be found in the sea. For perhaps twenty thousand years man has farmed the land. In the next twenty we must learn to farm the sea. There is little time to lose if we hope to feed our millions in the future.

Let us turn to another reason for our need of the sea. It is very likely that the sea will be the great recreation place of the future. Perhaps you have already put on flippers and a face mask and explored a little in the underwater world of the sea. Modern skin-diving gear has opened up a brand-new world of sport and underwater recreation.

197

With skin-diving gear man has discovered that the floor of the sea is the greatest museum in the world. Much of the wealth of mankind lies at the bottom of the sea in old sunken ships. Yet perhaps the greatest treasure in the sea is not gold or silver, but lost works of art. These have been lying in the mud on sunken ships for hundreds of years.

The sea holds both the past and the future of mankind. It is not empty, nor is it lifeless. It is our hope for tomorrow.

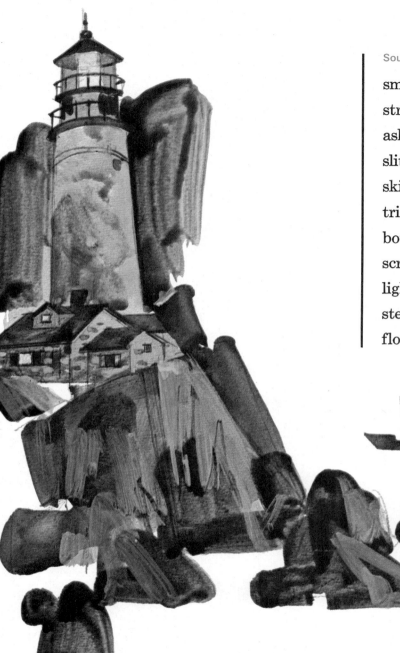

Sound the words.

smacked
stronger
ashore
slithered
skiff
trickle
bounded
scramble
lighthouse
stern
floundered

Seal of Frog Island

Ashore

John lived in a stone house at the bottom of a tall lighthouse on Frog Island. The island was well named. From a ship in the distance it looked like a big frog sitting quietly on the water. John's father was a lighthouse keeper, and his job was to keep the big light blinking at night.

One afternoon John was walking on the island when he suddenly heard a seal bark somewhere up ahead. John hurried along the rocky shore toward the sound, then stepped out on the sand beach. There it was—the smallest seal John had ever seen.

"Hello," John said, patting its furry brown head. "Where'd you come from?"

The seal looked up at John helplessly.

"Well!" John said. "I can't leave you here alone. You've lost your mother."

But John didn't know a thing about seals. So there was only one thing to do. He took the frightened baby in his arms and carried it home to the lighthouse.

John opened the door and tiptoed in. "See what I found!" he said.

Mother looked up and let out a little squeal. Father dropped his book.

"Can I keep it?" asked John.

"No!" said Father. "Why, it's so small it probably won't even be able to eat!"

But John felt sure Father was wrong. So he rushed out to the string of fish he had caught that morning and brought two little ones to the seal. The baby sniffed at the fish. But that was all.

Then Father carried the seal back to the water. "There are a lot of seals around," he said. "One of them may hear this baby barking and come find it."

At daylight the next morning John jumped out of bed. Quickly he put on his clothes and started outside to see if the baby seal had been rescued. But he tumbled over something lying in the doorway.

As John picked himself up, he heard a quiet little bark. There was the baby seal, settled in the doorway watching him.

"I guess we have a seal on our hands," said Father, shaking his head. "It probably hasn't eaten for a long time."

"How about some milk?" said Mother.

She poured some milk into an empty jar. Father found a rubber glove and stretched it over the jar. Then he cut a hole in one finger so the milk could trickle out.

The seal looked at John, but it did not try to drink. Then John wiped some milk gently on the seal's mouth. The baby seal smacked its lips and finally began to suck the milk with big noisy gulps.

But the seal needed more than just milk. So they stewed John's fish, mixed it with milk and oatmeal, and gave the seal some of that, too.

In a few days the little seal was eating more. It was John's job to catch the fish to go in its food. He always mixed the stewed fish with milk and oatmeal.

Each day the baby seal grew stronger. One day it jumped out of John's arms when he carried it down to the beach.

"Arf! Arf!" it barked. Then it snorted and bounded off in big slithery leaps. But the seal never went far from John. It had adopted John and his family. John named him Albert, and soon the little seal knew that was his name.

It was not long before John discovered that Albert couldn't swim. They were in the skiff fishing right off the beach when a sudden wave lifted the boat and dumped it over. John waded ashore, pulling the skiff behind him. But the seal floundered around helplessly. John started back to help. But when Albert caught sight of John, he seemed to understand what he had to do. And Albert began to swim ashore.

"Why, Albert, that's wonderful," said John, patting the seal's furry head. "I knew you could do it."

Later John told his father how Albert had floundered around until he finally swam ashore. "Yes," said Father. "Baby seals can't swim when they are little. They have to learn, just as children do."

Albert never forgot how to swim. He liked it so much that he often tried to pull John toward the water. John sometimes wished Albert would go swimming by himself. But Albert had adopted John as his mother, and he never went anywhere without him.

One day as soon as it was daylight, John took Albert fishing. Into the skiff they piled. John sat on the center seat to row. Albert climbed aboard and slithered onto a seat in the stern. "Now sit still, Albert," John said. "You'll tip over the boat."

At last John found his fishing spot. Then he settled down to catching fish. This was always a problem. Once he had a fish, it was a mad scramble to get it off the hook before Albert grabbed it.

John was sure the seal was old enough to catch his own fish. But he didn't know how to teach him to do it.

Sometimes when John put down his fishing pole, Albert picked it up in his mouth and dropped the line over the side. Then he sat there with the fishing pole in his mouth, trying to catch himself a fish. But Albert couldn't spend the rest of his life fishing with a pole.

Far down in the water John could see a fish. Well, he would fix that seal!

Quickly he grabbed Albert by the flipper and rolled him into the water. Albert went in with a splash. He barked and snorted and just as quickly bounded out of the water and piled back into the stern again. Then he picked up the fishing pole in his mouth and threw the line over the side.

"Oh, for goodness' sake! What a silly seal!" said John. "You don't even know you *are* a seal."

Then John had an idea. He held a nice fish in front of Albert. The seal smacked its lips and tumbled into the center seat. But instead of giving the fish to him, John threw it back into the water. Albert leaped about and watched it swim away.

John did the same thing again. The seal watched the fish swim away a second time. That was too much! The next time John threw a fish, the seal went after it. The fish swam awfully fast. Albert had a hard time catching it, but he did. And he looked very proud.

John patted him on the head. "You're a very smart seal, Albert," he told him.

Albert must have decided this meant a great deal, for at once he set out to catch more fish.

"Albert can feed himself," John told his mother and father that evening. "I won't have to stew his fish any longer. He's been catching fish all afternoon!"

Sound the words.

clank-clank

tower

balance

fuel

shivering

drooped

scold

enjoying

Lighthouse Trouble

Now that Albert could feed himself, John could spend more time enjoying him. And since Albert was such a smart seal, John thought he might be able to teach him some tricks. John knew that a seal could learn to balance a ball on its nose, so perhaps Albert could learn to do that.

John started out with his little rubber ball. He threw it to the seal, and Albert quickly reached out his nose, snapped up the ball in his mouth, and swallowed it in one gulp. Father and Mother laughed, and John clapped his hands. Albert thought that was pretty good himself, so he sat back and clapped his front flippers together. They were all excited because Albert had learned how to clap his hands.

John then got his big plastic beach ball. He held Albert's nose in the air and put the ball on top. And, sure enough, Albert could soon balance the ball on his nose.

John was pleased about Albert's tricks. Soon Albert learned many more.

One evening Father was enjoying a bath when suddenly John and Mother heard him shout, "Stop it, I say. Stop it!"

John and Mother both ran to the bathroom. Father was still sitting in the bathtub, and right in there with him was Albert. Father was smacking him on the nose with a washcloth.

"This is the last straw!" he said. "A man has a right to take a bath alone." Father glared at Albert, "Get him out of here!" But Mother laughed so hard she didn't have the strength to lift Albert.

The trick Albert loved most was rolling on the big kerosene drums. The kerosene was used as fuel for the big light in the tower. Albert would leap up to a drum lying on its side. And away it would roll, while Albert balanced himself on top of it. But Father did not like this trick.

"John, you're not to let that seal in the fuel shed at all," he said. "It's dangerous with all that kerosene stored there."

But every time Albert found the door open, he slipped into the shed. Rolling on one drum, he kept banging it into the others until someone heard the noise and came out to rap him on the nose. Father always shook his head and frowned, and John would scold Albert until he drooped away to hide.

Then one night John woke up hearing the clank-clank of the drums smacking into each other. Albert was riding on top of them in the fuel shed. Too sleepy to get up, John hoped Father didn't hear.

But Father had awakened, too. Far in the distance he had heard the whoo-whoo of a ship's horn. He had also heard Albert banging the fuel drums together. But he hardly gave this a thought.

Father jumped out of bed. Again he heard the ship's horn, closer this time. Quickly he ran to the door and looked up. The big light was out in the tower!

"John!" Father shouted. "Get some more oil. The light may have a leak!" Then he and Mother began to run up to the tower.

John took a lamp out of the shed and hung it on the door. Quickly he filled a bucket with kerosene and started back to the house. Out in the darkness the ship was blowing her horn as if calling to the light.

Up and up ran Father and Mother. Somehow the big light must be lit to warn the ship. Louder and louder came the ship's sound.

Quickly Father tried lighting the big light. But it was no use. He would have to light the small lamps. Mother's hand shook as she reached for the matchbox to help him.

They could see the lights of the ship still coming toward them.

Far below them in the shed, Albert had just fallen off a fuel drum. It rolled into the door where John's lamp hung. Crash! The lamp fell to the floor in flames. Albert scurried out of the shed. In his hurry he upset an open drum of kerosene. Splash! Big flames shot up with a terrible roar. The whole shed glared with hot flames.

"Albert!" John screamed, running back toward the shed. But it was too late. John stepped back as the heat hit his face.

Suddenly Albert came waddling up to him.
John caught the shivering seal in his arms.
"Oh, Albert!" he cried.

High above, Father stopped lighting the
lamps, and Mother cried out as she pointed
to the sea. The ship had seen the flames
and was turning away just in time.

Later, John and his family listened on
their radio to the ship as it made its way
up the coast. The captain praised Father
for burning the fuel drums. He asked that
Father be given a medal for saving the ship
and the lives of the crew.

Father patted Albert's head. "The medal
ought to be his," he said. "Playing in the
fuel shed was foolish, and we must never
let him do it again. But this time I'm glad
he was there. He saved the life of everyone
on that ship."

Sight word.

Michigan

Sound the words.

watertight
Columbus
overboard
drifting
Atlantic

Letter by Bottle Post

Have you ever written a secret message, put it in a watertight bottle, and tossed it into the waves?

Tim Williams did. In the middle of the ocean he tossed a bottle overboard from a ship. The note inside said—

> This bottle was put into the Atlantic Ocean midway between France and New York City.
>
> Would the person who finds this bottle please return the note to Tim Williams, 1121 Western Drive, Ann Arbor, Michigan, U.S.A., and tell when, and where, and by whom the note was found?
>
> Thank you very much.
>
> Tim Williams

A few months later Tim received a letter from a boy in France. His name was Alain Sargos. He had found Tim's bottle on the beach after a terrible storm. Alain wrote Tim a letter and sent him a picture of the beach. He had marked the picture with an X to show the spot where he had found the bottle.

Since then the boys have written several letters telling each other about themselves and their families. And the boys hope to meet someday.

Why would anyone choose to send a note in a bottle? One reason might be that no other way was possible.

In 1493 Christopher Columbus was sailing back to Spain to tell the king and queen about the world he had discovered. His ship came into a storm. Columbus was afraid he and his crew might be lost at sea and the news of the New World would never reach Spain. So he wrote a report on all he had discovered. Then he sealed it in a cedar box and threw it overboard.

Columbus reached shore safely, of course, so the floating box was forgotten. Many years later the box was found off the coast of Africa by the captain of a ship. However, this valuable message was later lost again, never to be found.

While Benjamin Franklin was America's Postmaster General, he discovered a new way to use floating bottles. American ships crossed the Atlantic Ocean faster than the ships from other countries, and Benjamin Franklin wondered why. He began to test certain ocean currents by tossing sealed bottles into the sea. And he found that some currents do move faster than others.

He made a chart of the currents. And after that, all men at sea could follow his chart to cross the ocean faster.

A bottle called "The Flying Dutchman" made the longest trip ever reported. This bottle belonged to German scientists. They put a letter inside that could be read without opening the bottle. It asked the person finding it to report when and where it was found and to throw it back into the water without opening it. The reports kept coming in. Then one day it was learned that The Flying Dutchman had gone all the way around the world.

One time a soldier wrote a love letter to his girl. He sealed the note in a bottle and threw it into the ocean. The note was delivered to the girl—but it had taken so long that she was a grandmother, seventy-eight years old, when she received it.

Strange things happen to drifting bottles. Two bottles dropped at the same time and at the same place might travel together. Or one of them might float away in a different direction. Some currents move bottles only one mile in a month, but others may carry them a hundred miles in one day. However, the speed of a drifting bottle is usually about one-half mile an hour.

Ocean scientists today use bottles to learn about the changing ocean currents. They toss bottles into the sea and keep track of their movement in the currents. Each bottle has a card inside which is to be returned to the scientists whenever it is found. More than two thousand of these cards are returned each year. Since fish also move with the currents, scientists can tell fishermen the places where fish can be caught.

One day, maybe you will find a bottle floating in the sea, or perhaps you will want to send one.

To send your message by bottle post, use a glass bottle with a narrow neck. This type is most easily made watertight. Put a little dry sand in the bottle so it will float slanting up. Write your message on a piece of paper, roll it up, and put it into the bottle. Cork the bottle tightly. If you have a nail, stick it into the cork and tie a flag to it so the bottle will be easy to see. Then toss your bottle as far out into the water as you can.

Maybe you will receive an answer to your message. Don't be disappointed if you have to wait a long time. It may drift and toss on the waves for many years. But sometime, somewhere, someone will shout excitedly, "Look! Here's a bottle with a note inside! I wonder where it came from."

It might be from you.

Sound the words.

chubby

aqualung

contest

explosive

diver

guy

timer

Hold Your Breath

223

Underwater Trap

It had all started when the Sharks had a contest to see who could stay underwater long enough to become a Tiger Shark. Web Williams came up first, and of course that made him last.

Like most chubby guys, Web could take a joke. But Red Sanders went too far. "Hey, chubby buddy!" Red yelled. "Need a rock to hold you down?"

Web ground his teeth and muttered to himself, "Wise guy!"

But Red wouldn't quit. "You got to stay down at least a minute to be a Tiger."

That did it. "Those smart guys bragging about becoming Tigers!" Web growled. "I'll show them! I'll learn to stay down for *two* minutes if it takes all summer!"

When school was out, Web and his family took off up the coast on vacation. That was perfect for Web because he'd just as soon practice in secret. The family spent most of the summer at the beach, and Web was the only person around who didn't have a tan.

He had spent so much time on the bottom of the harbor that his skin got to looking sort of wrinkled.

When Web finally got back home, he found Pete sitting on the pier.

"Hi!" Web called, trying not to act too excited. "Guess what! I can stay under for two minutes now!"

"Ha!" Pete said.

"Time me!" Web growled, taking off the watch he had won in a pie-eating contest. Then Web dived off the pier like a flat rock falling into the water.

On the bottom Web counted off a good two minutes, then pushed up to the top of the water. "How—did—I—do?" he gasped.

"Not bad, chubby buddy," Pete said. "Over two minutes, all right. But so what?"

"So what?" Web yelled as he climbed onto the pier. "How many other guys can stay down that long?"

"Well," Pete said. "Red Sanders has just been down about fifteen minutes."

Web whirled around just in time to see Red Sanders climbing out of the water. He had an aqualung!

"The whole summer wasted!" groaned Web. What did it matter now how long he could hold his breath? Guys with aqualungs could stay down almost forever.

Web thought about tying a big heavy rock around his neck and jumping off the pier.

But there was chocolate pie at home, so he decided to put off the rock idea awhile. Somehow he would become a Tiger Shark!

After a while, though, it looked pretty hopeless. None of the others could stay down even a minute anymore without the aqualungs, but that didn't matter. They could swim underwater as long as they wanted to, and Web began to feel like somebody with two left heads.

Right then was when the big television show came up, and the excitement about that sort of took his mind off his trouble.

"Listen," Leo Morelli told the Sharks. "You know my dad runs station KTTV. Well, they're going to do a TV show about that yacht that sank."

"The yacht with the safe full of money?" Pete exclaimed.

"Yes, but they won't bring up the whole yacht," Leo said. "They're going to blast open the safe underwater. But here's the important part. The Sharks get to help! They want us next Saturday, so show up with your aqualungs and skin-diving gear."

The Sharks all went wild about the big deal next Saturday—all except Web. He had wasted the summer holding his breath. And he didn't have an aqualung, so there was nothing he could do to help.

Web was at the pier on Saturday morning anyway. Even with nothing to do, it should be pretty exciting. Web sat on the pier and watched as a camera flashed test pictures of what was going on below.

Twenty feet down, the yacht rested in the sand. Suddenly on the television screen Web saw the Sharks swim up to the safe.

"Just look at those guys with Mr. Nelson, the head diver!" muttered Web. "Those lucky ducks!"

The Sharks swam around and pointed to the safe. It was all part of the show. And Pete really put on an act as he swam toward the camera. The camera flashed on Mr. Nelson. Carefully he placed the explosive charge by the safe. Then he set the timer.

"Ten more minutes and the explosive will go off," said the KTTV reporter, and Web shivered as he glanced at his watch.

Mr. Nelson had paused to close the cabin door. Suddenly the crowd on the pier gasped. Mr. Nelson's left foot had broken through a loose board on the deck. Quickly he tried to pull his foot free. But it was hopeless. Mr. Nelson was caught.

"The timer shows he's got only eight more minutes before that charge goes off!" Web exclaimed.

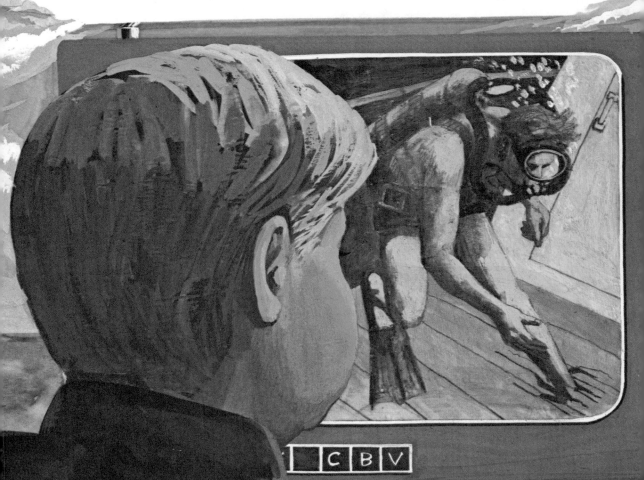

Sound the words.

moments
seconds
diving
nervously
gasping
plank
grease
churning

Race against Time

All at once Leo and Pete swam across the television screen. The boys pushed on the plank and tugged nervously at Mr. Nelson's foot. But it was no use. The plank would not give.

Then Leo pointed to a small hatch in the deck. Pete nodded. If they could get into the hold, they could pull the plank down and free the diver's foot.

"Only six more minutes!" Web groaned. "They've *got* to make it!"

230

The two Sharks reached the hatch and tore it free. Then there was a groan from the people on the pier. The air tanks on the aqualungs were so large that Pete and Leo couldn't get through the small opening to the hold.

"Five minutes left!" Web cried nervously. His stomach began churning. Then suddenly he got a crazy idea—like something Pete would have thought of. But, as he raced for the shed, Web knew he had to try it.

In the shed Web found what he wanted—a bucket of thick, black grease. He peeled off his clothes, and in ten seconds he had rubbed the sticky, black grease all over himself. And in ten more, he was on the pier and diving into the harbor.

Swiftly Web swam down through the cool, green water. The Sharks stared as their chubby buddy landed on the tilted yacht deck. Then Web began squeezing through the hatch. His greased body slipped through like a peeled grape. No trouble at all.

"Just let anyone kid me again about being fat!" he thought.

In the darkness inside the yacht Web felt
a moment of panic. Then he reached for Mr.
Nelson's trapped foot. Where was it? At
last he struck the diver's toes. Then he
moved his hands back a bit, his fingers
grabbing for the edges of the plank. He
could barely get a grip on it.

By now Web's heart was pounding in his
ears. And his lungs were burning for air.
He had to hurry. Web tugged on the broken
plank, but the board held tight. He thought
of the explosive—if he had any sense, he'd
give up and save himself.

In anger Web pulled again with all his might. The planking gave way all at once, banging Web against the side of the yacht. Mr. Nelson's foot was free.

Making a bubble trail, Web fought his way forward, trying to reach the hatch. He was dizzy and weak. He wondered if he could make it. Then eager arms pulled him swiftly through the opening. Web's lungs were on fire as he shot to the top.

Web had barely reached the pier when the explosive went off. For long seconds there was no picture on the television, only the churning darkness of water.

Gasping for air, Web thought of Nelson and himself down there, just moments ago. What if he hadn't practiced this summer? Suppose he hadn't been able to do it?

Then the Sharks were there, slapping Web on the back until it hurt and shaking his hand until he thought it would drop off.

"Welcome to the club, Tiger Shark!" they shouted.

"Tiger Shark?" Web gulped, still gasping for air. "You mean—"

"Sure!" said Red Sanders. "And from now on we spend half our time diving without aqualungs."

Mr. Nelson hobbled over, his foot in a bandage and his face somehow pale in spite of his tan. He started to say something, then stuck out his hand. That handshake meant more to Web than anything.

Web broke into a happy smile. Being a Tiger Shark was great, all right. But he suddenly remembered something else. He was still Web Williams, and he was hungry!

"Is there anything to eat around here?" he said, rubbing his greased stomach.

Then Tiger Web Williams, grinning as big as ever, headed for the nearest food.

Kathy B

235

Ever since Kathy could remember, she and her family had spent summer vacation on Harbor Island, one of a group of islands just off the mainland.

And almost as far back as Kathy could remember, she had wanted to learn to row. This summer she could row, but the boat had to be tied by a long line to an anchor on the beach. Dad demanded that the boat be tied until Kathy learned to swim.

She pulled hard on the long oars. Slowly the heavy rowboat moved toward a great rock covered with seaweed. On it sat a young herring gull as big as any grown-up herring gull. But Kathy knew it wasn't grown because it was still brown.

"You didn't have to be tied to a rope before you could fly alone, did you?" she said to the gull.

The boat jerked at the end of the line. The herring gull took off and caught an updraft of wind to sail high above Harbor Island. Kathy backwatered to shore, where her brother was building his own sailboat.

"You're lucky, Chris," she said. "You can go sailing in Little Harbor, around Middle Point, and into Big Harbor by yourself."

Chris's face showed that he understood how Kathy felt. "Patience, Kathy," he told her. "It wasn't long ago that I couldn't leave Little Harbor."

"Oh, Chris," Kathy said. "When will I be able to leave like you do?"

Chris grinned at her. "Like Dad said, whenever you can swim all the way out to the hauling line."

Kathy looked at the hauling line halfway out in the harbor. "Oh, if only learning to swim was as easy for me as rowing," she thought. "Whenever I take my hands off the bottom, I just sink!"

An hour later Kathy heard Chris shouting to the family. "Who's going with me to Ship's Cove for a swim?"

Kathy jumped down and ran into the house. Soon, in her swimming suit, she joined her family on the path. Chris led the way. Rog, Kathy's little brother, sat in a canvas seat high on Daddy's back. He was delighted to be taller than Kathy for once.

Kathy was the first one in the water. She repeated to herself what her mother had told her, "Reach over your head, pull down, and kick." Only this time instead of just saying it—she did it! She took two strokes before she touched bottom.

"Look at Kathy!" Chris shouted. "I think she's swimming."

The whole family waded in, including Rog.

"I'll bet she'll make it out to the hauling line before long," Dad said.

Each day after that she could take a few more strokes. She was really swimming, but still the hauling line seemed far away.

One morning Kathy was out in the rowboat again, still tied to shore. Rog demanded to come along.

"No, Rog! Mommy says you can't go in the boat unless she or Daddy is along," Kathy said. "You're not even three."

Later, when Kathy pulled the boat up on the shore, she let Rog help.

Mother called, "Lobster stew is ready!"

"Hurry up, Rog! Lobster stew!" Kathy called excitedly as she started up the hill.

She stopped at the woodshed to get Dad's permission to go with him to the mainland after lunch. Then she paused in the hallway to hang her life vest on its hook. In the kitchen she admired the flounder Chris had caught for supper.

As Kathy glanced away from the flounder, she happened to look out the window. There was the boat, drifting toward the hauling line. And Rog was sitting in it!

"Rog's out in the boat!" Kathy shouted as she dashed down the path. "He's untied the boat and isn't wearing a life vest!"

She kicked off her sneakers and waded out as far as she could. The boat was still beyond her. She began to swim. Reach, pull. Reach, pull, reach. And weary pull.

Just as the boat was drifting past the hauling line, Kathy grabbed it and climbed in over the stern.

Catching her breath, Kathy told Rog not to cry. She put the oars in the oarlocks—and Dad was there. He put Rog in the canvas seat and backwatered the boat to shore.

"Rog must have put the anchor in the boat and pushed himself off," Kathy said to her mother. "He wants to be as big as I am."

"Aren't we lucky to have a girl as big as you!" Mother replied.

"A girl whose boat won't be tied to shore any more," Dad added with a smile.

The next day when Dad came back from the post office, he brought a surprise. Riding in the wake of the boat and tied to the stern was a small rowboat with a blunt bow. It was painted blue on the inside and white on the outside.

"Wow! Is that a pram?" Chris shouted.

"It sure is," Dad replied. "How do you like it?"

Mother came running from the woodshed. "Good! You got the *Kathy B!*" she said.

"The *Kathy B?*" questioned Kathy.

"Oh dear, I've let out a secret!" Mother clapped her hand to her mouth. "I might just as well finish now. Daddy bought it for you last week. He knew you'd swim out to the hauling line very soon. The boat's name is to be the *Kathy B.*"

Kathy silently admired the boat a moment. Then she said softly, "Imagine that! The *Kathy B.*"

And a brown herring gull began to circle over her head in an updraft of wind, high in the sky.

Think about This:

1 Why do you suppose Dad demanded that the boat be tied until Kathy had learned to swim?
2 Do you think Chris is older than Kathy? Why?
3 Why do you think Rog went out in the boat alone?
4 Why didn't Dad buy the boat for both Chris and Kathy?

Sound the words.

swab

chowder

Admiral

gizzard

rafters

gale

ahoy

Sight words.

biscuit   onions

The Admiral
of Sandy Bay

A northeast gale was lashing the village of Sandy Bay the day Ronnie walked into Captain John's shop.

The opening of the door started a bell tinkling. Ronnie looked about.

"Steady as she goes. I'll be with you in a minute," a voice called.

Ronnie saw a man bent over a steaming kettle in the kitchen at the back of the shop. A smell of clam juice, hot milk, and onions filled the air. The man turned at that moment, showing a round, red face with full white whiskers.

"Haul alongside the stove, lad," said Captain John. "The clam chowder is ready."

"I didn't come for chowder," said Ronnie. "I haven't any money to spend."

"Money?" cried the Captain. "Who said anything about money? Me and the Admiral want your company. Don't we, Admiral?"

Ronnie glanced about for the Admiral. He saw nobody. Was the Captain a bit queer in the head?

Just behind him a hoarse voice muttered, "Slit his gizzard! Slit his gizzard!" The words were followed by a gasp and a shriek of mad laughter.

Something fluttered past Ronnie's head. He leaped aside with a cry. Then he felt rather silly. The noise had come from a parrot which landed on the kitchen table and rolled its eyes at Ronnie.

"Cut your throat? Cut your throat for a nickel, you swab!" cackled the parrot.

"Don't you mind the Admiral. He's taken a fancy to you. Not many people he likes," the Captain said.

Ronnie felt so flattered he offered the Admiral a bite of biscuit.

During the summer Ronnie spent a lot of time with the Captain and the Admiral. He counted them among his best friends.

One morning Ronnie found the Captain reading a telegram.

"I need to leave town for a few days," explained the Captain. "Ronnie, could you look after the Admiral while I'm away?"

"Of course," Ronnie agreed.

"I'll give you the key," said the Captain. "It gets chilly nights, and parrots catch cold easy. So just pop the Admiral in the cage at night and cover it with that big black cloth. You won't have any trouble. He's taken a real fancy to you."

That night at the shop Ronnie first made sure the doors and windows were locked. Then he called, "Ahoy, Admiral! Here's a biscuit. Time to get into your cage."

"Awrrrk," the Admiral squawked and hopped out of reach. Every time Ronnie came closer, the Admiral hopped aside.

"This won't do," thought Ronnie. He got the black cloth and threw it over the bird. The cloth jumped and twisted as the parrot struggled. Then the Admiral's beak clamped over Ronnie's thumb and sank deep. Ronnie let go. The Admiral burst out shrieking, then swooped up to his roost.

"You'll just have to stay there for the night," Ronnie said. But that night Ronnie worried. What if it did get chilly and the Admiral did catch a cold? What would Captain John think of Ronnie?

But the next morning Ronnie found the Admiral feeling fine. He flew down from the rafters and perched on Ronnie's shoulder. Then he cooed, "Cut your throat?"

"I'd like to cut yours," Ronnie said.

That day Ronnie tried setting a trap with a box to drop over the parrot. The Admiral watched from above, his head cocked to one side. Ronnie knew that his idea was no good because the Admiral just cackled at him.

The second night Ronnie built a small fire in the little stove. That sent some warm air up among the rafters where the Admiral chose to roost.

The third night it was dark, and a cold northeast gale was again lashing at Sandy Bay when Ronnie made his visit to the shop. A car was standing alongside the shop with its motor running. Its back seat was piled high with several large boxes.

"Must be someone on his way home after vacation," Ronnie thought.

He fitted his key into the door and heard the tinkling of the bell as it opened.

"Ahoy, Admiral!" Ronnie called. There was no answer. Behind him the door blew shut with a bang, and Ronnie jumped.

Then he felt along the counter for a box of matches to light the lamp. A board creaked across the room. Then it creaked again.

"Hey, Admiral!" Ronnie called.

"Shut up," said a hoarse voice as a heavy hand clamped across his mouth. On either side of Ronnie a man pressed close.

"Listen, you won't get hurt if you do what you're told. Understand?" said the hoarse voice again. Ronnie nodded. Then one of the men lighted a lamp.

Ronnie saw a canvas spread on the floor. On it the men had piled all the loot they could lift. These men were thieves!

Ronnie knew he could do nothing against these two huge men. Even if he screamed, no one would hear him.

"I haven't found the money, Nate," said the taller man.

"Now, boy, where does the old man keep his money?" Nate asked Ronnie.

"I don't know," gasped Ronnie.

"You just think hard!" growled the man.

"I don't know," Ronnie repeated. "Please believe me! It's the truth!"

The other man bent closer to Ronnie. He grabbed the boy's arm and twisted it. "Now talk fast, before—"

"Slit his gizzard," said a voice coming from the darkness. "Slit his gizzard."

The man let go of Ronnie and swung around. "Who's that? Put out the light!"

In the dark the strange voice muttered again. "Cut his throat."

The men ran for the back window.

"Help!" Ronnie shouted. "Help! Thieves!"

Then he wished he had kept still. When the Admiral heard Ronnie's voice, he started squawking, "Awrk, awrk, awrk!"

"It's a parrot!" shouted Nate. He turned his flashlight on the Admiral.

"Say, let's take the parrot along. I know where we can get a good price for him," said the other man.

"I think you're crazy, but catch him if you can, and we'll see," said Nate.

The man grabbed up the cloth and started after the parrot. The Admiral let out a shriek, swooped down on Nate's head, and grabbed his ear.

"Get him off!" Nate yelled. The other man tried to help, but the Admiral landed on the back of his neck and began biting.

At this point Ronnie ran out of the shop. When he returned with the village policeman and several neighbors, the two thieves were gone. But perched on an old rocking chair, in the middle of all the scattered loot, was the Admiral.

"Just think," cried Ronnie. "If I'd had my way, you'd have been shut up in your cage. Then you couldn't have fought off the robbers. You're a wise old bird!"

The parrot fluttered to his shoulder.

"Cut your throat?" he cooed. "Cut your throat for a nickel, you swab!"

Think about This:

1 Who do you suppose taught the Admiral to say the things he said?

2 What do you suppose Captain John thought when he returned and learned what had happened?

3 How do you think Ronnie felt when he said to the parrot, "I'd like to cut yours"?

4 What things in the story tell you that Captain John is a warm, friendly person?

Until I Saw the Sea

Until I saw the sea
   I did not know
   that wind
   could wrinkle water so.

   I never knew
   that sun
   could splinter a whole sea of blue.

   Nor
   did I know before,
   a sea breathes in and out
   upon a shore.

by Lilian Moore

Sound the words.

mysteries
lover
fables
Perrault
Aesop
slave
Germany
Denmark
Greece
shepherds

Sight words.

ancient   Arabian   Christian

Tales Told Forever

Long ago, before books were written, many hours in the evening were spent in telling stories. They were told and retold. And the best of all these stories were passed down by people in many countries, from grandfather to father to son. Many years later, different men throughout the world collected these stories and wrote them down to be kept in books. Because of such men, we can now read the old tales, and they will never be forgotten.

One of the most famous collections of old tales is *Aesop's Fables*. Aesop was not a collector of tales. He was a storyteller. Little is known about this man except that he was once a slave in ancient Greece. We also know that he told such tales as "The Fox and the Crow" to teach a lesson. It was left to the men living after Aesop to collect the old tales and put them in books so that we could enjoy them.

Two such collectors of tales lived in Germany. They were brothers who walked through the countryside listening to the stories being told by the German people.

The brothers heard stories about famous mysteries that were never solved, about strange things that had really happened, and about make-believe and magic. These stories had been told and retold throughout the years because the German people loved to hear them.

The brothers were school teachers. But after school they took time to write down the old tales they had heard in the German countryside. Today these tales may be found in a book called *Grimm's Fairy Tales*. And these men are now known as the famous Grimm brothers. It is in their book that we find such stories as "Hansel and Gretel" and "Rumpelstiltskin."

Another man who liked the old tales was Charles Perrault. He lived in France, and if you had been there, you might have seen him at a costume party. The men and ladies at these parties dressed like the shepherds who had watched over their sheep long ago. And they enjoyed telling each other stories about the old times in France.

After such a party Charles Perrault would go home and write down the tales he liked best. "Little Red Riding Hood" and "The Sleeping Beauty" were two of these stories.

They are in a book which he called *Tales of My Mother Goose.*

Another lover of the old tales was a man from Denmark named Hans Christian Andersen. Hans Christian liked to visit in a hospital near his home where the old women told him stories of the old days in Denmark. Hans Christian told the old women stories, too. He told them tales his father had read to him from a book called *The Arabian Nights.* Hans Christian was such a good storyteller he even made up stories of his own.

Today the stories of Hans Christian are in a book called *Andersen's Fairy Tales.* Perhaps you remember reading one of Hans Christian Andersen's stories called "The Emperor's New Clothes."

Some of these old stories have been told and retold in so many countries that we cannot tell where they first came from. Others are so much like tales from another country that we know they must be the same story. Each has simply been changed a little by people from different countries.

And that is what makes these old stories so much fun to tell. You can change a part of the story, take it out altogether, or add something to it. And if the story is better after you've changed it, perhaps someday someone will write it down the way you told it.

We have many old tales to enjoy because of the men who loved them, collected them, and wrote them down. But some old tales are lost to us. They were told and retold, but they were never written down.

Old American tales are still in danger of being lost—exciting cowboy tales once told around a campfire and tales of ancient Indians. Perhaps you can do something to keep stories of the past from being lost. If you hear an old story that you like, write it down. Then it, too, may never be forgotten.

Sound the words.

amazement
cleverness
richer
burgomaster
swiftest
cottage
interfering
decision
refused
advice

Sight word.

heifer

Clever Manka

261

There was once a rich farmer who was as greedy as he was rich. He was always driving a hard bargain and always getting the better of his poor neighbors. One of these neighbors was a shepherd who was to receive a heifer from the farmer in return for work. When it came time to pay, the farmer refused to give the shepherd the heifer. And the shepherd was forced to take the matter before the burgomaster.

The burgomaster, who was young and as yet not very experienced, listened to both sides. Then he said, "I will put a riddle to you both. The man who makes the best answer shall have the heifer. Agreed?"

The farmer and the shepherd agreed.

"Well," the burgomaster said, "here is my riddle. What is the swiftest thing in the world? What is the sweetest thing? What is the richest? Think out your answers and bring them to me at this same hour tomorrow."

The farmer went home in a temper. "What kind of burgomaster is this young fellow!" he growled. "I may lose the heifer, for I can't think of an answer to his riddle."

"What is the matter, husband?" his wife asked.

"It's that new burgomaster. The old one would have given me the heifer without any argument, but this young man thinks to decide the case by asking us riddles."

When he told his wife the riddle, she told him the answers at once. The farmer was delighted. "You're right, wife! That heifer is still ours!"

When the shepherd got home, he was sad. He had a daughter, a clever girl named Manka, who met him at the door of his cottage and asked, "What did the burgomaster say?"

The shepherd sighed. "I've lost the heifer. The burgomaster set us a riddle, and I shall never guess it."

"Perhaps I can help," Manka said. "What is it?"

The shepherd gave her the riddle, and the next day as he was setting out, Manka told him what answers to make.

When he reached the burgomaster's house, the farmer was already there. The burgomaster put the riddle to them again and asked the farmer for his answers.

The farmer began, "The swiftest thing in the world? That's my gray mare, of course, for no other horse ever passes us on the road. The sweetest? Honey from my bees, to be sure. The richest? What can be richer than my chest of golden ducats!"

"Hmmm," said the burgomaster. "Now what answers does the shepherd make?"

The shepherd bowed politely and said, "The swiftest thing in the world is thought, for thought can run any distance in the twinkling of an eye. The sweetest thing is sleep, for when a man is tired and sad, what can be sweeter? The richest thing is the earth, for out of the earth come all the riches of the world."

"Good!" the burgomaster cried. "Good! The heifer goes to the shepherd!"

Later the burgomaster said to the shepherd, "Tell me, now, who gave you those answers? I'm sure they never came out of your own head."

The shepherd tried not to tell, but he finally had to admit that they came from his daughter, Manka. Then the burgomaster thought that he would like to make another test of Manka's cleverness. So he sent for ten eggs and gave them to the shepherd.

"Take these to Manka and tell her to have them hatched by tomorrow and to bring me the chicks," he said.

When the shepherd reached home, he gave Manka the message. Manka just laughed and said, "Take a handful of millet and go right back to the burgomaster. Say to him, 'My daughter sends you this millet. She says that if you plant it, grow it, and harvest it by tomorrow, she'll bring you the ten chicks and you can feed them the ripe grain!' "

When the burgomaster heard this, he laughed heartily. "That's a clever girl!" he told the shepherd. "If she's as pretty as she is clever, I think I'd like to marry her. Tell her to come to see me."

When Manka was presented to the burgomaster, he was so delighted with her cleverness and so pleased with her good looks that he asked her to marry him.

"But understand, my dear Manka," he said, "I won't have you interfering in my cases. If ever you give advice to anyone who comes to me for a decision, I'll send you home to your father."

All went well for a time. Then one day two farmers came before the burgomaster.

One farmer owned a mare which had foaled in the marketplace. The colt had run under the wagon of the other farmer, and the owner of the wagon said the colt was his property.

The burgomaster, who was thinking of something else while the argument was being presented, said carelessly, "The man who found the colt under his wagon is the owner of the colt."

As the owner of the mare was leaving the burgomaster's house, he met Manka and stopped to tell her about the case. Manka was ashamed of her husband for making such a foolish decision.

"Come back this afternoon with a fishnet and stretch it across the dusty road," she said to the farmer. "When the burgomaster sees you, he will come out and ask what you are doing. Say to him that you're catching fish. When he asks how you expect to catch fish in a dusty road, tell him it's just as easy to catch fish in a dusty road as it is for a wagon to foal. Then he'll see that his decision was not fair and have the colt returned to you. But remember, you must not let him find out that it was I who told you to do this."

That afternoon the burgomaster looked out the window and saw a man stretching a fishnet across the dusty road. He went out to him and asked, "What are you doing?"

"Fishing," said the man.

"Fishing in a dusty road? Are you daft?"

"Well," the man said, "it's just as easy for me to catch fish in a dusty road as it is for a wagon to foal."

Then the burgomaster had to admit that what the farmer said was true. "Of course the colt belongs to your mare and must be returned to you," he said. "But tell me, who put you up to this? You didn't think this up yourself."

The farmer tried not to tell, but the burgomaster finally found out that Manka was at the bottom of it. This made him very angry. He went into the house and called his wife. "Manka," he said, "did you forget what I told you would happen if you started interfering in my cases? Home you go this very day! I don't care to hear any excuse. The matter is settled. But you may take with you the one thing you like best in my house."

"Very well, my dear husband," replied Manka. "But don't make me go until after supper. I should like to eat one last meal with you."

The burgomaster agreed, and Manka cooked a fine supper. The supper was so good that he ate and ate and ate. At last he fell sound asleep. Then Manka had him carried out to a wagon.

The next morning the burgomaster found himself in the shepherd's cottage.

"What does this mean?" he roared.

"Nothing, dear husband," Manka said. "You told me I might take with me the one thing I liked best in your house, so of course I took you! That's all."

For a moment the burgomaster rubbed his eyes in amazement. Then he laughed heartily and said, "Manka, you're too clever for me. Come on, my dear, let's go home."

The burgomaster never again scolded his wife, but thereafter when a very difficult case came up, he always said, "I think we had better ask my wife for advice. You know she's a very clever woman."

Sound the words.

scarcely

admiring

beaten

tortoise

Baba Outza

annoy

thatched

Why the Tortoise Has a Round Back

Long ago an old woman and her one little daughter lived in a tiny house in the heart of a forest. The thatched roof of her house was high and peaked so that the snow would slide off in the winter.

The old woman was not kind to her small daughter. She beat her for singing in the summer and made her shovel snow all day long in winter.

One day, when the old woman was making bread, two strangers came by.

"Baba Outza," they said, "will you make us some bread and give us something to eat?

We have come a long way, and we are very hungry."

The old woman looked at the men, who were tall and strong and beautiful and kind.

"Yes," she said. "If you will come back again in half an hour, I will give you something to eat."

She got a big pasteboard that she used to roll out bread dough. Then she set to work to make the bread. How good it looked, she thought, as she worked at it. So she shaped two loaves, one big loaf for herself and her little daughter, and one little loaf for the two strangers. She covered the big loaf and the little loaf with cloth and left them to rise.

"After all," she said to herself, "I do not know them. They said they were hungry, but who knows? I know that I am hungry. I have been working hard."

After a while she went to look at the loaves. When she lifted the cloth, she saw that the big loaf had scarcely risen at all. But the little loaf had grown so large that it was twice as big as the other.

"Well!" she said. "I shall keep the big one for myself and let the strangers have the little one!" So she popped them into the oven to bake.

When they were done, she opened the oven door. The little loaf was burned as black as coal, and it was as flat as it could be. But the big loaf was a fine golden brown loaf, beautiful and sweet smelling and soft. Now the old woman was cross.

"Just look at that!" said Baba Outza. "My loaf comes out big and fine. But the loaf for the strangers is all burned! What a pity! Now they can't have any bread."

And she took the burned loaf out into the yard and buried it in the rubbish heap.

Now it would not annoy the sun to see such an ugly burned loaf.

Then she went back into the house and began admiring the good loaf.

"Truly," she thought, "this is a very fine loaf of bread. It looks as though the angels had made it. Suppose the strangers come back! They will want a piece of it— and it is so fine and white! Oh, I cannot give them any of it. This loaf is mine. It is too good for them."

She called her little daughter.

"Listen," she said. "Listen to me, you naughty girl. Two strangers may come to ask for Baba Outza. They will say I promised them some fine bread. Tell them I have gone away on a long journey and will not be back. Do you hear?"

"Yes, Mother," answered the poor child, trembling for fear she would be beaten.

Then the old woman took the big pasteboard that she had used for rolling out the bread, and she put it on the floor. She got down on top of it and then turned to her daughter.

"Now!" she said. "Take the round trough that I mixed the bread in. Put it over me so that it covers me all up. Then the two strangers will believe you when you tell them I have gone away."

The little girl did as she was told. Then she stood in the doorway, waiting for the strangers to come. They soon came.

"Little girl," they said, "where is Baba Outza? She promised us some bread."

The little girl raised her eyes to the strangers. They saw the great tears standing in them.

"She has gone on a journey and will not be back for a long time," said the small girl, weeping. Her poor little heart hurt her, for she knew that what she said was not true.

The taller of the two men put his hand on her head.

"Where she is, there will she remain," he said. "But you will come with us. We will take you to a new home where no one will annoy you and you will not be beaten any more. You will be happy there."

And the two men took the little girl by her two hands and led her away to a home where she could be happy all the time.

But in Baba Outza's house nobody ate the fine white bread at all. For what do you think happened?

Baba Outza was changed into a tortoise. That is why tortoises are so old and ugly and wrinkled looking, and stick their heads and arms and legs out from under round, trough-like shells. They try to get out, but never can. Always and always Baba Outza has to wear the thin pasteboard on her stomach. Wherever she goes, she must remain with the round wooden trough she hid under. And she never has any bread, but has to live on leaves and grass.

Think about This:

1 Why do you suppose Baba Outza told the strangers she would make them some bread if she didn't really want to give them any?
2 What promises have you made that you later wished you hadn't?
3 Why do you think Baba Outza made her daughter lie to the strangers?
4 What other stories do you know that tell how animals became the way they are?

Sound the words.

contained

problems

argue

Greek

merchant

struggle

nobles

trudge

distant

The Clever Little Slave

Long ago in ancient Greece there lived a rich Greek merchant who owned many slaves. Among them was an ugly little man who was very clever.

One day the Greek merchant chose twenty of his best slaves for a trip to a distant city. "Here are twenty sacks," he said. "This journey will take many days, so each of you may choose the sack you will carry. But mind you! Once you have chosen, you cannot change!"

Instantly there was a wild scramble as each slave tried to pick as small a sack as possible. But there was one man who did not join the rush. The ugly little slave just stood by quietly and waited until the others had chosen. Then he walked over and picked up the remaining sack. It was the biggest sack of the lot, almost as big as the little man himself. But with a smile he swung it onto his shoulders and joined his companions.

How the others laughed! "Was ever a man so foolish, little one," they cried. "You have chosen the biggest sack of all.

And now you must carry it for the whole journey. Oh, ho, ho! Ha, ha, ha!"

The little man staggered under the weight of the huge sack. But he grinned cheerfully and said, "Oh well, someone must carry it. Besides, this sack contains magic of a sort. Perhaps all of you will soon wish you had chosen it."

Day after day the slaves wound their way along rough mountain trails. But soon they noticed a strange thing. The little slave's sack was growing smaller. As days passed, it grew smaller and smaller. At last the slaves saw how wise the little man was.

For the sack he had picked up contained food for the journey. And, of course, after each meal there was less to be carried. At the end of the journey the little slave walked into town, swinging an empty sack. But his companions' sacks were just as heavy as when they had started.

Because of this and many other ways in which the little man showed how wise he was, the rich merchant began to notice him.

"What is your name?" asked the merchant.

"My name is Aesop," replied the slave.

The merchant decided that Aesop was too wise to be a slave, so he set him free. The other slaves were happy for Aesop, but they also felt sad because he was leaving. Aesop had often made their work easier by telling them stories.

It was wonderful to be free, but Aesop soon learned that freedom had its problems. Since he had been a slave almost all his life, he knew no trade by which he could earn his bread. There was only one thing he could do. He could tell stories.

The kind of story Aesop told is called a fable. In this kind of story animals talk and act like people, and each story usually teaches a lesson of some kind.

Aesop visited the marketplaces of Greek towns and told his stories in exchange for food. And before long, people all over Greece heard of the clever little slave who told such wonderful stories. Finally the king of Greece heard of him and invited Aesop to come live at the palace and be the court storyteller.

By now the little slave was weary of trying to think of new stories. So he became storyteller to the king and entertained the nobles of the court with his fables.

The people of Greece never grew tired of Aesop's fables. And when books were printed, Aesop's fables became popular all over the world. "The Wind and the Sun," "The Man, the Boy, and the Donkey," and "The Fox and the Crow" are three of the fables told by the clever little slave so long ago.

The Wind and the Sun

A long time ago, the Wind and the Sun began to argue about which was the stronger. Suddenly they saw a traveler coming down the road.

"I see a way to decide our argument," said the Sun. "Whichever of us can cause that traveler to take off his cloak shall be the stronger. You begin."

So the Sun went behind a cloud, and the Wind began to blow as hard as it could upon the traveler. But the harder it blew, the more closely the traveler wrapped his cloak around him. At last the Wind had to give up in despair.

Then the Sun came out and began to shine in all its glory upon the traveler. Soon the traveler found it too hot to walk with his cloak on.

"There!" said the Sun. "My kindness was much stronger than your force."

The Man, the Boy, and the Donkey

A man and his son were once going with their donkey to market. As they were walking along by its side, a countryman passed them. "You fools, what is a donkey for but to ride upon?" said the countryman.

So the man put his son on the donkey, and they went on. Soon they passed some men, and one of them said, "See that lazy boy. He lets his father walk while he rides."

So the father ordered his son to get off and got on himself. But they hadn't gone far when they passed two women. "Shame on that lazy man to let his poor little son trudge along," one of them said.

Well, the man didn't know what to do, but at last he took the boy up before him on the donkey. By this time they had come to the town. The people passing by began to laugh and point at them. The man stopped and asked what they were laughing at.

"Aren't you ashamed of yourself?" they said. "Overloading that donkey of yours— you and your hulking son."

The man and his son got off and tried to think what to do. They thought and thought. At last they cut down a pole and tied the donkey's feet to it. Then they raised the pole and the donkey to their shoulders. They went along amid the laughter of all who met them until they came to the market bridge.

There the donkey, getting one of its feet loose, kicked out and caused the boy to drop his end of the pole. In the struggle the donkey fell over the bridge. Then it got its forefeet untied and ran away.

"That will teach you," said an old man who had been following them. "Please all, and you will please none."

The Fox and the Crow

A fox once saw a crow fly away with a piece of cheese in its beak and settle on a branch of a tree. "That's for me, as I am a fox," said the fox to himself. And he walked up to the foot of the tree.

"Good-day, Mrs. Crow," he cried. "How well you are looking today! How glossy your feathers are! And how bright is your eye! Your voice is surely more lovely than that of other birds, just as your figure is. Let me hear just one song from you so that I may greet you as the Queen of Birds."

The crow lifted up her head and began to caw her best. Instantly the piece of cheese fell to the ground and was quickly snapped up by the fox.

"That will do," said the fox. "That was all I wanted. In exchange for your cheese I will give you a piece of advice—never listen to anyone who flatters you."

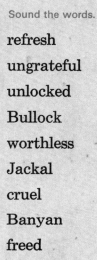

Sight word.

Brahmin

Sound the words.

refresh

ungrateful

unlocked

Bullock

worthless

Jackal

cruel

Banyan

freed

The Brahmin, the Tiger, and the Jackal

289

Do you know what a Brahmin is? A Brahmin is a very good and gentle kind of man who treats all the beasts as if they were his brothers. There is a great deal more to know about Brahmins, but that is enough for the story.

One day a Brahmin was walking along a country road when he came upon a Tiger shut up in a strong iron cage.

"Oh, Brother Brahmin," said the Tiger. "Please let me out. I am so thirsty, and there is no water here in this cage."

"But, Brother Tiger," said the Brahmin. "You know that if I should let you out, you would spring on me and eat me up."

"Oh, never, Brother Brahmin!" said the Tiger. "I would not do such an ungrateful thing! Just let me out to get a drink of water, Brother Brahmin!"

So the Brahmin unlocked the door and let the Tiger out. The moment he was out of the cage, the Tiger sprang on the Brahmin and was about to eat him up.

"But, Brother Tiger," cried the Brahmin. "You promised you would not! It is not fair that you should eat me, when I'm the one who set you free."

"That was when I was in the cage," said the Tiger. "But now that I am free, I shall eat you up."

The poor Brahmin wept and begged. At last the Tiger agreed to wait and ask the first five whom they should meet whether it was fair for him to eat the Brahmin. The Tiger also agreed to act by their decision.

The very first thing they met was an old Banyan Tree, standing by the wayside.

"Brother Banyan," said the Brahmin. "Does it seem fair that this Tiger should eat me, when I set him free from his cage?"

"In the summer," said the Banyan Tree, "when the sun is hot, men sit in the cool of my shade and refresh themselves with the fruit from my branches. But when evening falls and they are rested, they break my twigs, scatter my leaves, and shake my limbs for more fruit. Men are ungrateful! Let the Tiger eat the Brahmin!"

The Tiger sprang to eat the Brahmin. But the Brahmin cried, "Wait! We have asked only one. We have still four to ask!"

Presently they came to a place where an old Bullock was lying by the road.

"Brother Bullock," said the Brahmin, "is it fair that this Tiger should eat me up, after I have freed him from a cage?"

"When I was young and strong," replied the Bullock, "my master used me hard, but I served him well. Now that I am old and weak and cannot work, he leaves me without food or water to die by the wayside. Men are a thankless lot! Let the Tiger eat the Brahmin!"

The Tiger sprang, but the Brahmin spoke quickly, "This is only the second, Brother Tiger! You promised to ask five!"

The Tiger grumbled a good deal, but at last he went on with the Brahmin. Soon they saw an Eagle, high overhead.

"Oh, Brother Eagle," the Brahmin called. "Does it seem fair to you that this Tiger should eat me up, when I have just saved him from a frightful cage?"

The Eagle came lower. "I live high in the air," he said. "And I do no man any harm. Yet, men stone my young and rob my nest and shoot at me with arrows. Men are cruel! Let the Tiger eat the Brahmin!"

The Tiger sprang upon the Brahmin to eat him up.

"But, Brother Tiger, we have two more to ask!" cried the Brahmin.

"Very well!" growled the Tiger. "But I am very hungry."

Before long they saw an old Alligator, lying in the mud at the river's edge.

"Brother Alligator," said the Brahmin. "Does it seem fair to you that this Tiger should eat me up, when I have just now let him out of a cage?"

"I lie here in the mud all day, as harmless as a dove," the old Alligator grunted. "I hunt no man. Yet every time a man sees me, he throws stones and pokes me with sharp sticks. Men are a worthless lot! Let the Tiger eat the Brahmin!"

At this the Tiger was bound to eat the Brahmin at once. But the Brahmin begged, "Wait until we have asked one more!"

Finally the Tiger walked on with him.

After a time they met a little Jackal. "Oh, Brother Jackal!" said the Brahmin. "Do you think it is fair that this Tiger should eat me, when I set him free from a terrible cage?"

"Cage?" said the Jackal stupidly.

"Yes, yes, his cage," said the Brahmin. "We want to know what you think—"

"Oh," said the little Jackal. "Then may I beg you to speak more loudly and make the matter quite clear? I am a little slow of understanding. Now what was it?"

"Do you think," said the Brahmin, "it is right for this Tiger to eat me, when I set him free from his cage?"

"What cage?" asked the little Jackal.

"Why, the cage he was in," replied the Brahmin. "You see—"

"But I don't really understand," said the Jackal. "You freed him, you say?"

"Yes, yes, yes!" exclaimed the Brahmin. "It was this way. I was walking along, and I saw the Tiger—"

"Oh, dear, dear!" said the little Jackal. "I never can see through it, if you go on like that, with a long story. If you really want to know what I think, you must make the matter clear. What sort of cage?"

"Why, an iron cage," said the Brahmin.

"That gives me no idea at all," said the Jackal. "See here, my friends. If we are to get on with this matter, you'd best show me the spot. Then I can understand quickly. Show me the cage."

So the Brahmin, the Tiger, and the little Jackal walked back together to the spot where the cage was.

"Now, let us understand the problem," said the little Jackal. "Brahmin, where were you?"

"I stood here by the roadside," said the Brahmin.

"And, Tiger, where were you?" asked the little Jackal.

"Why, in the cage, of course!" roared the Tiger.

"Oh, I beg your pardon, Brother Tiger," said the Jackal. "I really am stupid and cannot quite understand what happened. *How* were you in the cage? What were you doing inside the cage?"

"I stood here," said the Tiger, leaping back into the cage, "with my head over my shoulder, so."

"Oh, thank you, thank you," the little Jackal said. "That makes it *much* clearer.

But I still don't quite understand. Forgive my slow mind. Why did you not come out by yourself?"

"Can't you see that the door shut me in?" cried the Tiger.

"Oh, I do beg your pardon," the Jackal said. "I know I am very slow. I can never understand things well unless I see just how they were. If you could show me now *exactly* how that door works, I am sure I could understand. How does it shut?"

"It shuts like this," said the Brahmin, pushing the door to.

"Yes. But I don't see any lock," said the little Jackal. "Does the door lock on the outside?"

"It locks like this," said the Brahmin. And he shut and bolted the door.

"Oh, does it indeed?" the little Jackal exclaimed. "Does it *indeed!* Well, Brother Brahmin, now that it is locked, I should advise you to let it stay locked! As for you, my friend," he said to the Tiger, "you will wait a good while before you'll find anyone to let you out again!"

Then the little Jackal made a very low bow to the Brahmin.

"Good-bye, Brother Brahmin," smiled the Jackal. "Your way lies that way. And mine lies this. Good-bye!"

Think about This:

1 Why do you suppose the Brahmin set the Tiger free?
2 Most of the animals said, "Let the Tiger eat the Brahmin!" Why?
3 Do you think the Jackal was really slow to understand? Why?
4 If the Brahmin met another animal caught in a cage, do you think he would free it? Why?

Sound the words.

dwarf

velvet

refuse

brew

miller

spin

larger

Elsa

halt

spools

Rumpelstiltskin

301

CAST:

Miller	First Soldier
Elsa	Second Soldier
King	Third Soldier
Dwarf	Storyteller

Scene I

Storyteller: Once upon a time there lived a poor miller who had a beautiful little daughter. As she grew older, he wondered how he would find a good husband for her. One day he said to his daughter,

Miller: I am beginning to worry about you, Elsa, my child.

Elsa: Worry? Why, Father?

Miller: It is time for you to marry, but I have no money to give to a husband.

Elsa: Then who will marry me, except a man as poor as we are?

Miller: You have no money, but you are a very beautiful girl—beautiful enough to be a queen.

Elsa: (*Laughs*) A queen! Oh, Father!

Miller: (*Thoughtful*) Yes, a queen! If only the King could see you!

Elsa: The King? How could I ever get in sight of the King?

Miller: If he ever saw you, Elsa, I'm sure he would wish to make you his queen. Now, how can I make that happen? Ah! I think I have an idea!

Elsa: What is it, Father?

Miller: I must tell it to the King first. Go on with your spinning while I think it out.

Storyteller: The next day the miller and his daughter went to the King's palace. A soldier stopped them at the gate.

First Soldier: Halt! Who goes there?

Miller: A miller, soldier. I live down by the river.

First Soldier: And this girl?

Miller: She is my daughter, my beautiful daughter, Elsa.

First Soldier: What would a miller and his daughter want with the King? Go to the kitchen if you want to sell flour.

Miller: I must see the King himself. I want to do him a favor. Let me pass, if you please.

First Soldier: You, a poor miller, want to do the King a favor?

Miller: Yes. You see, my daughter can do something wonderful. She can spin straw into gold.

Elsa: Oh, Father! What are you saying?

First Soldier: Oh? That is something the King would really like to see. He always needs gold. You may go into the throne room.

Sound: (Door opens.)

Elsa: Father! Don't go!

Miller: Thank you, soldier. Wait here, Elsa.

Sound: (Door shuts.)

King: Well, who are you, man? What do you want?

Miller: Your Majesty, I have a beautiful daughter.

King: Is that all you have to say? There are many beautiful girls here.

Miller: My daughter is not only beautiful. She can do something wonderful. She can spin straw into gold!

King: Well, that is something else. I always need gold and more gold.

Miller: Yes, Your Majesty. If you will only see her.

King: Straw into gold! Bring her here this afternoon.

Miller: Your Majesty, my daughter is waiting outside this room.

King: Ah! So much the better! Soldier, take the miller's daughter into one of the rooms. See that it is filled with straw and have a spinning wheel put in, at once.

Second Soldier: At once, Your Majesty.

Miller: Wouldn't you like to watch my beautiful daughter as she spins, Your Majesty? Just one look?

King: No. Now go, miller, and tell your daughter to start spinning at once. If she does not spin all the straw into gold by morning, she shall die.

Miller: Oh! Your Majesty! But—

King: Go, I said. Soldier, see that the girl is locked in the room all night. Go, now, both of you.

Storyteller: Elsa, the miller's daughter, was locked in the room full of straw. She was told to spin the straw into gold by morning or die. Poor Elsa didn't know what to do. She started to cry.

Elsa: Oh, dear! What shall I do? What?

Dwarf: (*Cross, gruff voice*) Good afternoon, miller's daughter.

Elsa: Oh my! Where did you come from, little man?

Dwarf: I came through the keyhole. Why are you crying, miller's daughter?

Elsa: The King has ordered me to spin all this straw into gold by morning. If I don't, I must die. Why, I don't even spin wool very well.

Dwarf: What will you give me if I spin it into gold for you?

Elsa: Oh, could you spin it for me? I have no money, but I'll give you my velvet hair ribbon.

Dwarf: All right! It's a bargain. Now let me sit down at the spinning wheel.

Scene 2

Storyteller: The little man spun and spun until all the straw was gone and all the spools were full of gold. Then he was gone as quickly as he had come. Early the next morning the King came.

Sound: (Door opens.)

King: Ah! Gold! So you really can turn straw into gold.

Elsa: You see the gold before you, Your Majesty.

King: Lovely, shining gold! Now, miller's daughter, you shall be put into a larger room of straw. Spin it into gold before morning, if you love your life.

Elsa: But, Your Majesty—

King: Soldier, have a larger room filled with straw and take the spinning wheel and the girl into it.

Soldier: It shall be done, Your Majesty.

Storyteller: So Elsa was taken into a much larger room which was filled with straw for her to change into gold. She looked at the straw and began to cry.

Dwarf: Good-day, miller's daughter.

Elsa: Oh! The little man again! I'm so glad to see you! Please, will you help me again today?

Dwarf: Tell me first, what will you give me if I spin this straw into gold?

Elsa: I will give you the gold ring from my finger.

Dwarf: Very well! Give me the ring. Now let me sit at your spinning wheel.

Storyteller: The next day, when the King came to the room, he looked at the spools of gold and smiled. This time he looked at the miller's daughter, too. He saw that she was beautiful, but he wanted still more gold. He led her into an even larger room filled with straw.

King: You must spin for me one night more, miller's daughter.

Elsa: But, Your Majesty, I cannot.

King: Why not? You have done it twice. Do you refuse to do it again?

Elsa: Oh, no, Your Majesty, but—

King: If it is all spun by sunrise, you shall become my queen.

310

Elsa: Oh, Your Majesty! How can I—

King: How can you, a poor girl, marry a king? Why you can spin more gold than any princess ever has. Not another word, now. Set to work.

Elsa: (Weeps) Oh, dear! If only the little man would come again!

Dwarf: Here I am, miller's daughter.

Elsa: Oh! Thank goodness you've come to me again! Please, will you spin for me this third time?

Dwarf: What will you give this time?

Elsa: Oh, dear! I have nothing left to give you.

Dwarf: There is one thing for which I will spin tonight.

Elsa: What is that?

Dwarf: Promise that when you are Queen you will give me your first child.

Elsa: Who knows if I shall ever become Queen? Very well, little man, I promise that if I become Queen you shall have my first child.

Dwarf: That's what I want! Now I'll sit down and spin.

Storyteller: Early the next morning the King came again and found the room full of spools of gold.

King: Ah! More gold! How the room shines with its light!

Elsa: Your Majesty is pleased!

King: I am, and I shall keep my promise. You shall be my queen.

Elsa: Oh, Your Majesty!

King: Now that I look at you well, I see that you are really as beautiful as your father said.

Elsa: Thank you, Your Majesty. I shall try to be a good queen.

King: I shall call for the ladies of the palace to dress you for our wedding.

Scene 3

Storyteller: So the miller's daughter and the King were married, and they were very happy. About a year later the Queen had a beautiful little son. By this time she had forgotten all about the little man and her promise to him. But one night, as she sat with her baby in her arms, the little man came into her room.

Dwarf: Good evening, Queen.

Elsa: Oh! The little man who helped me spin the straw!

Dwarf: Yes, indeed. Now you must keep your promise. Give me your child.

Elsa: Oh, no, no! I can't give him up! I can't.

Dwarf: But you promised!

Elsa: Oh, I know I promised. But it was to save my life. Oh, please, kind little man! I'll give you anything else you say— gold, jewels, anything! But not my baby! I love him so!

Dwarf: Nothing else will do. But I'll give you one chance to keep your baby.

Elsa: What is it? I'll do anything.

Dwarf: I'll give you three days to find out my name. If you do that, you shall keep your child. If you don't guess my name, you must give him to me, just as you promised.

Elsa: Oh, thank you, little man, for this chance. I'll try to guess your name.

Dwarf: (*Strange laugh*) You'll have to try very, very hard!

Storyteller: The Queen did not want to tell the King about the little man. She lay awake all night thinking of all the names she had ever heard. The next night the little man came again.

Dwarf: Well, Queen, what do you think my name is?

Elsa: Is your name Henry?

Dwarf: (*Laughs*) No.

Elsa: Is it John?

Dwarf: (*Laughs*) No.

Elsa: Is it Joseph? William? Arthur? George? (*Dwarf laughs after each name.*)

Dwarf: It isn't any name you have ever heard. My name is so strange that you'll never, never guess it.

Storyteller: The next day the Queen sent soldiers out to learn all the queer names that they could. When night came, she cried as she waited for the dwarf.

Dwarf: Well, Queen, do you think you know my name now?

Elsa: Is your name Shorty?

Dwarf: No, it is not.

315

Elsa: Is your name Spindleshanks?

Dwarf: No, it's not.

Elsa: Are you called Crosspatch?

Dwarf: No, I'm not called any of these. You have one night left to try to guess my name. If you can't guess it then, I shall have your child!

Storyteller: The Queen was very worried that third day. Each soldier came back saying he had heard no new name. But the last soldier told a strange story.

Third Soldier: Your Majesty, I saw a very strange sight today.

Elsa: Will it help me guess the little man's name?

Third Soldier: Perhaps. I was coming through a dark forest. I came to a tiny house. I walked quietly to the window and looked in. Hopping up and down before the fire was a strange little man. As he hopped he sang,

"Today I brew, tomorrow I bake,
Next morning I the Queen's child take.
How glad I am she does not know
My name is Rumpelstiltskin!"

Elsa: That must be my little man! Thank you for your good news. Take this piece of gold as a reward.

Third Soldier: Thank you, Your Majesty.

Storyteller: Soon after the soldier was gone, the little man came into the Queen's room again.

Dwarf: Well, Queen, this is your very last chance. What is my name?

Elsa: Are you called Conrad?

Dwarf: No.

Elsa: Is your name James?

Dwarf: No.

Elsa: (Smiling) Then your name must be— Rumpelstiltskin!

Dwarf: (*Angry*) The fairies must have told you! The fairies must have told you! (*He stamps his foot.*)

Elsa: Now you can't take my baby! Stamp your foot as hard as you like! Ah! You have stamped your foot into the ground, and you can never pull it out!

Dwarf: The fairies must have told you! (*He stamps his other foot.*)

Elsa: Oh! Now your other foot is deep in the ground! Why, the little man is sinking! He's gone! Now he'll never be able to harm my baby.

Storyteller: Yes, the little man sank down into the ground and was never seen again. And the Queen kept her baby and was very happy.

ACKNOWLEDGMENTS

Grateful acknowledgment is given for permission to adapt and reprint the following copyrighted material:

"The Admiral of Sandy Bay" adapted from "Ronnie and the Admiral" by Jack Bechdolt. *Story Parade Magazine*, May 1948. Used by permission of Ellen A. Merwin.

"Answers from the Sea." The adaptation of the chapter "The World of Water" from *The Challenge of the Sea* by Arthur C. Clarke has been made by permission of the publishers, Holt, Rinehart and Winston, Inc. Copyright of *The Challenge of the Sea*, © 1960 by Arthur C. Clarke. Reprinted by permission of the author and the author's agent, Scott Meredith Literary Agency, Inc.

"Azor and the Turtle" adapted from *Azor* by Maude Crowley. Copyright 1948 by Henry Z. Walck, Inc. Used by permission of the publisher.

"Beyond the Footlights" adapted from the story "The Big Dream" by Lea Walker from *Story Parade Magazine*. Copyright 1953 by Story Parade, Inc. By permission of Western Publishing Company, Inc.

"Bobcat on the Run" adapted from "Bobcat on the Run" by Peter Churchward from *Boys' Life* Magazine, copyright 1963 Boy Scouts of America. Reprinted by permission of Collins-Knowlton-Wing, Inc., the author, and *Boys' Life*, published by the Boy Scouts of America.

"The Brahmin, the Tiger, and the Jackal" adapted from "The Brahmin, the Tiger, and the Jackal" from *Stories to Tell to Children*, edited by Sara Cone Bryant. Houghton Mifflin Company, publisher.

"Buffalo Dusk" reprinted from *Smoke and Steel* by Carl Sandburg, copyright, 1920, by Harcourt Brace Jovanovich, Inc., renewed, 1948, by Carl Sandburg. Reprinted by permission of Harcourt Brace Jovanovich, Inc.

"City Child" from *We Live in the City*, by Lois Lenski. Copyright, 1954, by Lois Lenski. Reprinted by permission of J. B. Lippincott Company.

"The Clever Little Slave" adapted from "The Clever Little Slave" by Murray T. Pringle. Copyright 1954 by Story Parade, Inc. Adapted and reprinted by permission of Western Publishing Company, Inc.

"Clever Manka." Copyright 1920 by Parker Fillmore; renewed 1948 by Louise Fillmore. Adapted from "Clever Manka" in *The Shepherd's Nosegay* by Parker Fillmore, edited by Katherine Love, by permission of Harcourt Brace Jovanovich, Inc.

"The Copper Kettle" adapted from "The Copper Kettle" retold by Alice Geer Kelsey, *Story Parade Magazine*, July 1940. Used by permission of the author.

"Dreams" reprinted from *The Dream Keeper* by Langston Hughes. Copyright 1932 by Alfred A. Knopf, Inc. and renewed 1960 by Langston Hughes. Reprinted by permission of the publisher.

"Glassmaker's Street" adapted from the story "Glass-Maker's Street" by Frances Rogers from *Story Parade Magazine*. Copyright 1939; copyright renewed 1967 by Story Parade, Inc. By permission of Western Publishing Company, Inc.

"Great Day at Salem" adapted from the story "Salem's Great Day" by F. J. Jupo from *Story Parade Magazine*. Copyright 1948 by Story Parade, Inc. By permission of Western Publishing Company, Inc.

"Hold Your Breath" adapted from "Hold Your Breath" by D. S. Halacy, Jr., *Boys' Life* Magazine, May 1960. Reprinted by permission of the author and *Boys' Life*, published by the Boy Scouts of America.

"Janey's Shoes" adapted from "Janey's Shoes" by Ellis Credle. Original version appeared in *Story Parade*, May 1942. Used by permission of the author.

"Kathy B" adapted from "The Cruise of the *Kathy B*" by Polly Welts Kaufman. Adapted by special permission from *Jack and Jill* Magazine © 1965 The Curtis Publishing Company.

"Konok's Trade" adapted from the story "Treasures of the Sea" by Frances W. Kittredge from *Story Parade Magazine*. Copyright 1938; copyright renewed 1966 by Story Parade, Inc. By permission of Western Publishing Company, Inc.

"Letter by Bottle Post" adapted from "A Letter by Bottle Post" by Emily Rhoads Johnson. Adapted by special permission from *Jack and Jill* Magazine © 1968 The Curtis Publishing Company.

"Little Alligator" adapted from the story "Little Alligator" by Dorothy Pierce Lehman from *Story Parade Magazine*. Copyright 1943; copyright renewed 1971 by Story Parade, Inc. By permission of Western Publishing Company, Inc.

ILLUSTRATORS

Ted Carr, Gus Colichidas, Vickie Erickson, Lowell Herrero, Tom Hill, David Kerr, Earnie Kollar, Rebecca Lusk, William Mathison, Tom Newsom, Bert Rosamond, Bill Simon, Philip Smith, Bill Stebbins, Al Stine, Joe Szeghy, Jerry Warshoski, Darrell Wiskur.